HEAD, HEART AND HAND

PARTNERSHIPS FOR WOMEN'S HEALTH IN CANADIAN ENVIRONMENTS

Volume II

Published by:
National Network on Environments and Women's Health
York Centre for Health Studies, 214 York Lanes
York University
4700 Keele Street
Toronto, Ontario M3J 1P3
Telephone: 416 736 5941 Fax 416 736 5986
Email: nnewh@yorku.ca
Web site: www.yorku.ca/nnewh

The National Network on Environments and Women's Health (NNEWH) is financially supported by the Women's Health Contribution Program, Women's Health Bureau, Health Canada. The views expressed herein do not necessarily represent offical policy of Health Canada.

Printed and Bound in Canada by Webcom.

Cover Design/Interior Design: Luciana Ricciutelli
Cover Art: Lisa Lipsett, "Umbilicus," acrylic/oil on masonite, 24" x 32", 2002

National Library of Canada Cataloguing in Publication Data

Head, heart and hand: partnership for women's health in Canadian environments/edited by Penny van Esterik

ISBN 1-55014-410-3 (v.1).—ISBN 1-55014-427-8 (v. 2)

1. Women--Health and hygiene--Canada. 2. Women's health services--Canada.
I. Van Esterik, Penny II. National Network on Environments and Women's Health

RA564.85.H43 2003   362.1'082'0971   C2003-905879-4

HEAD, HEART AND HAND

PARTNERSHIPS FOR WOMEN'S HEALTH IN CANADIAN ENVIRONMENTS

Volume II

EDITED BY PENNY VAN ESTERIK

NATIONAL NETWORK ON ENVIRONMENTS AND WOMEN'S HEALTH
RÉSEAU PANCANADIEN SUR LA SANTÉ DES FEMMES ET LE MILIEU

Contents

Introduction

The National Network on Environments and Women's Health (NNEWH) is one of four remaining federal Centres of Excellence for Women's Health established in1996 by the Women's Health Contribution Program and mandated to "enhance the health system's understanding of and responsiveness to women's health." Each of the Centres was to accomplish this goal through research that would generate and contribute to the development of new knowledge and information about women's health, networking, and policy advice. Specifically, NNEWH's mandate was to create a national network of social researchers and community partners who would develop new ways to identify and interpret women's health experiences. We chose to focus those efforts on the ways in which three key environments (namely work, health systems, and policy) act as determinants of women's health.

In our early years, we devoted considerable time to the development of organizational operations and infrastructure. We funded projects that promoted novel methodology, ground-breaking research, and productive partnerships. Between 2000 and 2002, we turned our attention toward improved communications within and beyond the network and to the increasingly critical arena of policy advice. We entered our seventh year of operations with a firm foundation on which to build stronger relationships and partnerships and a renewed spirit of commitment and contribution to the development of new knowledge and policy advice pertaining to women's health in Canada. Now in our eigth year of operation we are continuing to strengthen our community-academic partnerships and to prosper from the ways in which they enhance our knowledge base about women's health and appropriate health policy.

NNEWH's community and academic partners have always shared the objective of ensuring that health policies are appropriately and creatively developed in response to evidence-based findings on the social conditions of women's health. In spite of the tensions created and the significant investment in time and financial resources demanded, our partnership model is a key aspect of the work we do. It provides for different perspectives, promotes synergy of ideas and resources (knowledge is enhanced, financial, personnel, and infrastructure resources go farther), enhances opportunities for practical spin-offs, increases public accountability and is a marvellous tool for educating academics and the public. In addition, partnerships increase opportunities for dual top-down and bottom-up approaches when recommending policy changes. Much of the work in these two volumes reflects this synergy.

Specifically, however, the work behind the publication of these two volumes reflects the care and commitment of the editor, Penny Van Esterik. As is often the case, it became a much larger and more time consuming project than we thought it would be at the outset. Nevertheless, she prevailed and *Head, Heart and Hand* was produced. Thank you, Penny, for your commitment to capturing this set of literature and making it easily accessible to others. We would never have succeeded without you.

*****

Le Réseau pancanadien pour la santé des femmes et le milieu (RPSFM) est l'un des quatre Centres d'excellence pour la santé des femmes toujours en activité, mis sur pied en 1996 grâce aux fonds fédéraux du Programme de contribution pour la santé des femmes et ayant pour mandat « de comprendre davantage la question de la santé des femmes et d'amener le système de santé à mieux répondre aux besoins de celles-ci ». Chaque Centre devait réaliser cet objectif par le biais de recherches qui généreraient de nouvelles connaissances et de l'information ou qui contribueraient à de nouvelles découvertes dans le domaine de la santé des femmes, tout en favorisant le réseautage et les interventions-conseils en matière de politiques. Notamment, le mandat du RPSFM était de créer un réseau pancanadien de chercheuses sociales et de partenaires communautaires qui développeraient de nouvelles façons d'identifier et d'interpréter le vécu des femmes sur le plan de la santé. Nous avons choisi de concentrer nos efforts sur l'identification des conséquences générées par trois éléments clés (c.-à-d. le travail, les systèmes de santé et les politiques) qui agissent comme déterminants de la santé des femmes.

Au cours de nos premières années, nous avons consacré beaucoup de temps à l'élaboration du fonctionnement organisationnel et de l'infrastructure. Nous avons financé des projets qui promouvaient de nouvelles méthodologies et qui généraient des recherches innovatrices et des partenariats fructueux. Entre 2000 et 2002, nous avons porté notre attention sur l'amélioration des communications au sein et au-delà du Réseau et sur le travail de plus en plus important d'intervention-conseils en matière de politiques. Nous avons entamé notre septième année d'activités avec une assise solide qui nous permettait de construire des liens et des partenariats plus forts, et un esprit renouvelé favorisant l'engagement, le développement de nouvelles connaissances et la prestation de conseils à l'échelle des politiques reliés à la santé des femmes au Canada. Nous en sommes maintenant à notre huitième année et nous continuons à consolider nos partenariats entre le monde communautaire et le monde de la recherche et à profiter des apprentissages que nous en tirons pour élargir notre base de connaissances sur la santé des femmes et sur les politiques de santé appropriées.

Les partenaires des milieux communautaires et des milieux de la recherche œuvrant dans le cadre du RPSFM ont toujours partagé le même objectif : veiller à ce que les politiques de santé soient pertinentes et élaborées de façon créative et en réponse aux découvertes fondées sur des preuves et liées aux conditions sociales influant sur la santé des femmes. Malgré certaines tensions et l'investissement important en temps et en ressources financières inhérents à une telle démarche, notre modèle de partenariat constitue un aspect essentiel de notre travail. Il suscite des perspectives différentes, stimule la synergie d'idées et de ressources (approfondissement des connaissances, possibilités d'accomplir davantage avec les ressources en fonds, en personnel et en infrastructures), augmente les possibilités de retombées concrètes ainsi que la capacité de reddition des comptes, et constitue un excellent outil pour sensibiliser les chercheuse(eur)s et le public. De plus, le recours aux partenariats augmente les possibilités d'une démarche descendante et ascendante lors du processus de recommandations pour changer les politiques. Une grande part du travail entourant la réalisation de ces deux volumes reflète cette synergie.

Toutefois, les efforts qui ont mené à la publication de ces deux volumes reflètent tout particulièrement l'application et la détermination de la rédactrice, Penny Van Esterik. Comme c'est souvent le cas, le projet s'est avéré beaucoup plus grand et beaucoup plus long que nous ne l'avions prévu au départ. Malgré tout, elle a tenu bon et les volumes *Tête, cœur et action* ont été réalisés. Merci Penny d'avoir embrassé la grande tâche de rassembler tous ces documents et de les rendre accessibles au public. Nous n'aurions jamais réussi sans toi.

Frances M. Shaver
Chair, NNEWH Executive
Présidente, direction du RPSFM
October/Octobre 2003

Editor's Preface
Préface de la rédactrice

Head, Heart and Hand: These are not the words that flow trippingly off the tongues of academics. I first heard them used by Anwar Fazal, a Malaysian consumer advocate and health activist, the founder of Health Action International, who also heads the NGO partner I represent in the National Network on Environments and Women's Health (NNEWH), the World Alliance for Breastfeeding Action (WABA). I later heard this special trio of words spoken in different languages by women's groups and health activists in their participatory work in many different communities. I was also reminded that head, heart, hand and health is the motto of the 4-H youth clubs. The phrase stresses the kinds of partnerships necessary to make changes in civil society that will hopefully benefit women's health in the short and long term. The words also epitomize the nature of partnerships that NNEWH encourages between academic researchers, community health advocates and policymakers. Knowledge production—whether in the heads of academics or activists—does not take us far if there is no will to put it into effect; and all of us must contribute to the hands-on work of knowledge translation. NNEWH is comprised of head, heart and hands-on people and groups; it is also committed to integrating all three in its practices; as a network, we try to recognize that head, heart and hand groups have different needs, resources and priorities. Hence the title.

We are in addition delighted to feature the work of artist/environmental educator, Lisa Lipsett, on the cover. Her work, *Umbilicus,* was part of a series called *Being with Child,* shown at the Muskoka Arts and Crafts Gallery in Bracebridge, Ontario in the spring of 2003. Although the papers in these volumes focus on a wide assortment of issues and concerns relating to women's health, reproduction is an important topic of special interest to many women. *Umbilicus,* moreover, is a particularly effective metaphor for the connections NNEWH has given birth to and nourished over the past few years.

Selection Process

In May, 2003, I took on the task of furthering a project envisioned by NNEWH's directors, committees and partners—making some of the many papers, reports, and other written products submitted to NNEWH over the last few years available to a larger audience. Many papers fell into the category of "fugitive literature"—workshop reports, commissioned literature reviews, handouts—that slip too easily between the cracks of regular library cataloguing. Reading all materials submitted to NNEWH was a fascinating but time-consuming task; in addition I reviewed memos referring to the future production of a compendium of NNEWH papers. The research reports confirmed the fact that the words and activities of NNEWH partners have much to say about the health situation of Canadian women. With the assistance of members of the editorial committee, I selected papers and reports that presented a complete project or argument, and had not already been published in book form or in widely distributed journals. For example, several project reports were revised, published and circulated in books such as *Exposing Privatization: Women in Health Care Reform in Canada*, edited by Pat Armstrong and colleagues (2002, Garamond Press), and *The Gender of Genetic Futures: Canadian Biotechnology, Women and Health*, edited by Fiona Miller and colleagues (NNEWH, 2000). The editorial team reasoned that these edited volumes have already had an impact on policy makers and did not need to be reproduced in the compendium. Instead, we looked for papers that, while based on local research, would be of general interest to Canadian researchers and health activists, and had not yet received wide distribution. We worked hard to limit the size of papers, but readily admit that we were not always successful in keeping all contributions to a manageable size. Cutting papers in size often required removing graphics, tables and appendices. If we could not cut the paper in length without destroying the integrity of the piece, or if authors were unable to meet our tight deadlines for approving edited proofs, papers were not included. These longer papers as well as all NNEWH reports can be obtained from NNEWH, or from our website (www.yorku.ca/nnewh/).

The papers are divided into two volumes. Volume One represents lengthy, more theoretical work undertaken by NNEWH partners. Volume Two contains shorter more practical pieces, often produced and used by community groups. Yet both volumes are advocacy based in the sense that they are meant to shift prevailing values with regard to women's health in Canada. Community groups are welcome to make use of the workshop formats, handout sheets, and bibliographies in volume two for their own information kits, acknowledging NNEWH as their source.

As a network concerned with healthy working environments, we chose Webcom for printing, a "green" printer whose policy includes offering the most environmentally responsible choices to customers. The paper used in these publications is elemental chlorine-free.

Acknowledgements

Inspiration for this compendium comes from Georgina Feldberg, the principal investigator for the original NNEWH grant, Marilou McPhedran, the former executive coordinator of NNEWH who began the process of coordinating compendium work, and Kimberly Walker, the current executive coordinator who joined NNEWH in July, 2003 and brought these two volumes to completion. All NNEWH partners contributed to the energy and excitement that culminated in the products included here. Although the full papers are written in English the abstracts have all been translated into French. In addition, several of the papers are available in French on the NNEWH website.

The editorial committee members, Frances Shaver, Chair of the NNEWH Executive Committee; Cecilia Benoit, chair of NNEWH Research, Network and Training Committee; Gail Lush, Agnieszka (Iggy) Kosny, and Gwen Wood helped with some of the more difficult last minute decisions that accompany this form of publishing. Over the course of the production, a number of students and staff assisted in the process, including Myagmartseren (Miga) Chultem, Zestaline Kim, Sandra Kerr and Lauren Johnson. I am particularly grateful to Lauren whose eye for detail, computer skills and persistent follow-up kept me and these publications on track. Thanks also to Luciana Ricciutelli, our production editor, who worked quickly with a wide range of materials to produce an integrated attractive publication in the midst of blackouts and other human impediments.

York University has assisted NNEWH in numerous ways, particularly through the efforts of Suzanne MacDonald, Associate Vice-President for Research. The York Centre for Health Studies (YCHS) houses NNEWH, and continues in partnership with NNEWH under the leadership of Marcia Rioux, director of YCHS, and head of the School of Health Policy and Management at Atkinson Faculty of Liberal and Professional Studies.

Finally, we are grateful to the Women's Health Bureau (WHB), Health Canada, NNEWH's funder, and to Catherine Kulisek, the manager of the Centres of Excellence Women's Health Program, WHB. All research reports and publications in these volumes carry the disclaimer that the views expressed do not necessarily represent official policy of Health Canada, as do these volumes.

*****

Tête, cœur et action. Ce ne sont pas des mots que le monde de la recherche prononce souvent. La première fois que je les ai entendus, ils venaient d'Anwar Fazal, une militante malaysienne pour les droits des consommatrice(teur)s et pour le droit à la santé. Fondatrice de Health Action International [Action santé internationale], elle dirige également l'ONG partenaire que je représente dans le Réseau pancanadien pour la santé des femmes et le milieu (RPSFM), la World Alliance for Breastfeeding Action (WABA) [Alliance mondiale pour l'allaitement]. J'ai entendu ces trois mots prononcés en plusieurs langues par des groupes de femmes et des militantes en santé, dans le cadre de leur travail auprès de multiples communautés diverses. Ces mots mettent l'accent sur la nécessité d'établir des partenariats pour créer des changements au sein de la société civile, lesquels, nous l'espérons, favoriseront la santé des femmes à court et à long termes. Ils incarnent aussi le type de collaboration que le RPSFM encourage entre chercheuse(eur)s, militante(ant)s en santé communautaire et décisionnaires. Les connaissances, qu'elles soient produites par des chercheuse(eur)s ou des militante(ant)s, donnent peu de résultats si la volonté de les mettre en pratique est inexistante, et nous devons toutes et tous contribuer au travail concret de la conversion du savoir. Le RPSFM est fait de personnes et de groupes qui font un travail de tête, de cœur et d'action. Il est voué également à l'intégration de ces trois dimensions dans ses pratiques. En tant que réseau, nous reconnaissons que les groupes qui œuvrent à l'échelle de la tête, du cœur et de l'action possèdent des ressources, des priorités et des besoins différents, d'où le titre.

Nous sommes également heureuses de présenter sur notre page-couverture l'œuvre de Lisa Lipsett, artiste et éducatrice environnementale. Sa création, *Umbilicus*, fait partie d'une série intitulée *Being with Child* [Femmes enceintes], présentée au printemps 2003 à la galerie d'art et d'artisanat de Muskoka, en Ontario. Bien que les articles de ces publications traitent d'un large éventail de questions et de préoccupations reliées à la santé des femmes, la reproduction est un important sujet qui intéresse nombre de femmes. De plus, *Umbilicus* est une métaphore particulièrement efficace qui fait référence aux liens que le RPSFM a tissés et nourris au cours des dernières années.

Processus de sélection

En mai 2003, j'ai accepté la tâche de poursuivre un projet mis au monde par les directrices, les comités et les partenaires du RPSFM, soit de rendre accessibles à un public élargi les nombreux articles, rapports et autres documents soumis au RPSFM au cours des dernières années. Nombre de documents ont été classés dans la catégorie « documentation fuyante »—des rapports d'ateliers, des critiques de documents réalisées sur commande, des tracs—trop facilement rejetée dans le processus de catalogage traditionnel appliqué en bibliothèque. Toute en étant fascinante, la lecture des documents soumis au RPSFM a exigé beaucoup de temps. De plus, j'ai relu des notes de services qui traitaient de la création d'un recueil de documents du RPSFM. Les rapports de recherche confirmaient que les propos et les activités des partenaires du RPSFM offraient beaucoup d'information sur la situation des Canadiennes en matière de santé. Avec l'aide de membres du comité de rédaction, j'ai sélectionné des articles et des rapports qui présentaient un projet ou une argumentation de façon complète et qui n'avaient pas été publiés sous forme de livre ou dans des revues à grand tirage. À titre d'exemple, plusieurs rapports de projets ont été révisés, publiés et diffusés dans des livres, tels qu'*Exposing Privatization: Women in Health Care Reform in Canada* [La privatisation mise à nue : les femmes dans le cadre de la réforme de santé au Canada] , publié sous la direction de Pat Armstrong et collègues (2002, Garamond Press), et *The Gender of Genetic Futures: Canadian Biotechnology, Women and Health* [Les rapports sociaux entre les sexes et les scénarios d'avenir en matière de génétique : la biotechnologie canadienne, les femmes et la santé], publié sous la direction de Fiona Miller et collègues (RPSFM, 2000). Selon l'équipe de rédaction, ces volumes édités avaient déjà exercé un impact auprès des décisionnaires et n'avaient nul besoin d'être reproduits dans un recueil. Nous avons plutôt examiné des articles qui, bien qu'issus de recherches régionales, présentaient un intérêt général pour les chercheuse(eur)s canadienne(ien)s et les militante(ant)s en santé, et qui n'avaient pas encore été grandement diffusés. Nous avons travaillé assidûment pour limiter la longueur des articles mais nous avouons d'emblée que nous n'avons pu réduire adéquatement tous les documents. La réduction d'articles nécessite souvent l'élimination des graphiques, des tableaux et des annexes. Quand nous ne pouvions réduire certains articles sans détruire l'intégrité de l'œuvre ou lorsque les auteure(eur)s ne pouvaient approuver les versions révisées en respectant notre échéancier serré, les articles étaient alors exclus du recueil. Vous pouvez toutefois obtenir ces articles plus volumineux et tous les rapports du RPSFM en vous adressant au Réseau ou en consultant notre site Web (www.yorku.ca/nnewh/).

Les articles sont divisés en deux volumes. Le premier présente des œuvres volumineuses et plus théoriques réalisées par des partenaires du RPSFM. Le deuxième contient des documents moins volumineux et plus pratiques, qui sont souvent produits et utilisés par des groupes communautaires. Toutefois, les deux volumes sont axés sur la défense des droits et leur objectif est notamment de transformer les valeurs dominantes dans le domaine de la santé des femmes au Canada. Les groupes communautaires peuvent intégrer les plans d'ateliers, les tracs et les bibliographies présentés dans le deuxième volume dans leurs propres trousses d'information, à condition de mentionner le nom du RPSFM comme source.

La question de le salubrité des milieux de travail est importante pour le Réseau et nous avons choisi Webcom pour imprimer le recueil, un imprimeur « vert » qui offre à sa clientèle un choix de processus des plus respectueux de l'environnement. Le papier utilisé pour ces publications ne contient aucun chlore élémentaire.

Remerciements

Ce recueil est né des personnes suivantes: Georgina Feldberg, directrice des recherches sous la subvention originelle du RPSFM; Marilou McPhedran, ancienne coordonnatrice du RPSFM qui a amorcé la coordination des travaux; et Kimberly Walker, coordonnatrice exécutive actuelle qui s'est jointe au RPSFM en juillet 2003 et qui a mené à terme la réalisation de ces deux volumes. Tous les partenaires du RPSFM ont contribué au climat d'énergie et d'enthousiasme qui a imprégné le projet, un climat qui a donné lieu au contenu de ce document. Bien que les articles eux-mêmes soient en anglais, les résumés ont tous été traduits en français. De plus, plusieurs des articles sont disponibles en français sur le site Web du RPSFM.

Les membres suivantes du comité de rédaction ont pris les décisions plus difficiles de dernière minute, inhérentes à ce type de publication : Frances Shaver, présidente du comité exécutif du RPSFM, Cecilia Benoit, présidente du comité de recherche, de réseautage et de formation du RPSFM, Gail Lush, Agnieszka (Iggy) Kosny et Gwen Wood. Au cours de la production, des étudiantes et des membres du personnel ont participé aux tâches, dont Myagmartseren (Miga) Chultem, Zestaline Kim, Sandra Kerr et Lauren Johnson. Je remercie particulièrement Lauren, dont le sens du détail, les connaissances en informatique et les suivis continus m'ont aidée à garder le cap et ont assuré la qualité des publications. Je remercie également Luciana Ricciutelli, notre chef de production, rédactrice en chef de Inanna Publications and Education inc., qui a travaillé rapidement, avec un large éventail de documents, et qui a produit une publication intégrée et de belle apparence malgré les pannes d'électricité et les obstacles de nature humaine.

L'Université York a aidé le RPSFM de nombreuses façons, notamment par le biais de Suzanne MacDonald, vice-présidente associée chargée de la recherche. Le RPSFM loge dans les locaux du York Centre for Health Studies (YCHS). Le Centre poursuit son partenariat avec le Réseau sous le leadership de sa directrice, Marcia Rioux, qui dirige également la School of Health Policy and Management, à la Atkinson Faculty of Liberal and Professional Studies.

Pour terminer, nous remercions le Bureau pour la santé des femmes (BSF), de Santé Canada, qui finance le RPSFM, ainsi que Catherine Kulisek du BSF, directrice du programme des Centres d'excellence pour la santé des femmes. Tous les rapports de recherche et publications inclus dans ces volumes contiennent un avis précisant que les points de vue exprimés ne reflètent pas nécessairement les politiques officielles de Santé Canada.

Penny Van Esterik
Department of Anthropology/Département d'Anthropologie
York University/Université York
September/Septembre 2003

SECTION I: WORKSHOPS

Strategic Workshops
Planning and Design

KRISTINE HIRSCHKORN, DEPARTMENT OF SOCIOLOGY, MCMASTER UNIVERISTY
WORKING GROUP ON WOMEN AND THE NEW GENETICS

The following report was commissioned by the Working Group on Women and the New Genetics (WGWNG), an adjunct group of the National Network on Environments and Women's Health (NNEWH) and the Centres of Excellence in Women's Health Program.

The intent of this report is to present models, case studies, resources and general information for the design and implementation of an effective strategic workshop. This report does not address the general planning of conferences, but rather focuses on factors that differentiate a strategic workshop from a conference format. Specifically, the report is intended to inform the preparation of a proposed strategic workshop of the WGWNG, with special relevancy given to address the community/academic consultative process as well as the broadly defined goals of the WGWNG. However, the contents of this report speak to the planning and design of strategic workshops generally, and are applicable to initiatives outside of the WGWNG's mandate.

The report contents are derived primarily from telephone interviews with the primary organizers of four conferences in the field of New Genetics and Genetic and Reproductive Technologies, namely:

- "NRTs… The Contradictions of Choice: The Common Ground Between Disability Rights and Feminist Analysis," held in Vancouver in November, 1994.
- "Disability Rights in Dialogue with Clinical Genetics," held in the U.S. in May 1996.
- "Genetic Information: Acquisition, Access and Control (WAGICS)," held in the U.S. in May, 1996.
- "National Dialogue on Genetics," held in the U.S. in March, 1998.

These conferences were chosen as a resource because of their emphasis on a feminist and women-centred forum for approaching the issue of New Genetics. Representation at the conferences was generally cross-sectoral, with a strong emphasis on community group participation. Organizers made special efforts to include (or to attempt to include) women of colour and women with disabilities. Each of these factors is of relevance to the goals/objectives of the WGWNG's proposed strategic workshop. In addition to conference materials provided by the organizers, other resources drawn on are listed in the bibliography at the end of the text.

The contents of this report are broadly divided into three sections. The first section, titled "Workshop Preparation," presents some questions that organizers need to work with, in order to establish the parameters of the workshop. Suggestions for the composition of the organizational team, participant lists, and preparatory communication/materials are made. Section two, "Workshop Structure" discusses the role of facilitators/mediators and identifies informal and formal models for interactive group work. The third section, "Follow-up/Continuity of Networking" discusses options for maintaining communications between workshop participants. The summary presents suggestions made by informants and also contextualises workshop objectives by outlining a framework of how strategy is generally formulated for responding to identified issues.

I. Workshop Preparation

A suggested optimal length for a strategic workshop, especially for an initial problem identification, is two to three days. Where multi-sectoral and varied social/economic status groups are to be included, it has also been suggested that several, rather than one, workshop be organized, each tailored to a specific target group of participants, in order to ease communication difficulties and provide for a better focus for each individual workshop. Much of the contents of this report are adaptable to a multi-workshop scheme.

What's Involved? Objectives and Goal Setting

Foremost, determine what the objectives of the workshop are, relative to longer-term goals, and maintain a clear focus throughout. Consider both process and outcome. For example:

- What specific outcomes of the strategic workshop are needed in order to meet the proposed goals of communications/networking, research, education and policy impact?
- Is consensus sought or needed in order to proceed? How important is the formulation of recommendations and action plans?
- How does the group consultative process relate to desired outcome? Are process and outcome objectives consistent? Note that for community-academic consultation, a fair (i.e. "equal") consultative process should be a central objective.
- How much and what kind of conflict is constructive? When will it interfere with objectives? Identify and disclose potential conflict in order to facilitate clear lines of communication.

When setting an agenda, frame some specific questions that will become the focal point of the workshop. Clear objectives will help to determine participant list as well as other audiences.

When inviting participants, be sure they are aware of and agree to work with the workshop objectives. The workshop must be operating from a platform that is clearly defined *before* participants sit down around the table. As one informant stated, "dump the rhetoric" and disclose intent.

Resources

Be sure of financial resources before concretising plans. Do not be over-ambitious. Overextending your capacity will lead to frustration for all involved and will not be conducive to further networking/communication nor to meeting defined objectives. It is better to stay small and focused than to attempt to work outside of your means.

Organizational Team

In addition to a planning committee that oversees the work and makes key decisions, the following individual positions are recommended:

•Planning Committee Chair to act as liaison between planning committee, assistant(s) and co-ordinator; to provide introductory remarks/welcome at workshop.

•Workshop co-ordinator (may also be workshop chair) to oversee and participate in planning. This is potentially a very time-consuming position and may amount to as much as 20 hrs/week as workshop date approaches.

•Administrative/communications assistant to aid co-ordinator for duration of planning and after workshop date (to edit report and follow-up documents, facilitate networking, etc.). A minimum of 10 hrs/week, preferably more, would be recommended. As workshop date approaches, hours would likely increase. Responsibilities of co-ordinator and assistant overlap.

•Neutral third-party facilitator/mediator should be involved (even minimally) before the workshop date. Suggestion: a facilitator with an academic affiliation might best be avoided. She should be experienced in working with mixed, and especially community, groups in order to balance what is generally a strong academic presence in workshop planning. Refer to Section II: "Workshop Structure" below for a more detailed description of facilitator role.

•Other: logistic support for duration of workshop for participant registration, note-taking if deemed necessary, photocopying and reproduction of needed materials, relay of communication, and for various errands that arise throughout the day.

Workshop organizers speak frequently of "burn-out," long hours and high stress as the workshop/conference date approaches. Conference organising tends to overload individuals who already work full-time doing other activities and many of whom are volunteering time. Be sensitive to these stresses and pressures when assessing human resources needs. Likewise, be sure individuals are committed for the duration. Changing team members, especially the co-ordinator, assistant and facilitator/mediator part way through is disruptive and contributes to the loss of both time and focus. Here again, being sensitive to the pressures and time commitments involved on the part of the organising staff can help to avoid these disruptions.

Participant List

Emphasis again is on clarity/focus. Choose participants based on expressed objectives of workshop. Be inclusive, however acknowledge that the line has to be drawn somewhere, and that you cannot let people in just because they want to be there. It is acceptable to make these choices and exclusions, however criteria must be clearly outlined and the process must be transparent.

Some considerations:

•What kind of contribution do you want participants to make? Here, the question is not just "who they are" but "how they are" in group negotiation. Avoid inviting angry factions and maintain a focused agenda so that the most difficult voices do not "hijack" the proceedings. If participants are not prepared to work within the workshop objectives and framework, then there is little point in having them present. Workshop activity needs to be constructive, not destructive. This does not mean that the participants must agree on the issues, only that they need to agree to work toward objectives of workshop and communicate with the group, which means accommodating other participants' differences.

•Role of group participants: their individual attitudes and methods of participation affect group dynamics; their willingness to deal with (inevitable) tension and disagreement without becoming disillusioned or angry is important. Frame the terms of reference for participants by specifying in prep materials the importance of each individual's contribution to and responsibility for facilitating the learning/negotiation process. This is a component of outlining workshop objectives.

•Be aware of who knows who and how this will affect group interaction. Camaraderie and already-established networks/ties can leave other participants feeling left out. Provide for a balance. For example, be aware of how a workshop organized by academics will affect the non-academic participants. The role of the facilitator/mediator is key to dealing with these group dynamics.

•Identify stakeholders who are they, or how are they to be included?

 •Do not choose participants for "optics," choose them based on objectives. One informant suggested, "get participants who have information, do research, are articulate, get some consumers, get 'movers' and 'shakers', not token people."

 •Marginalised groups—Aboriginal people (Native, Métis, Inuit), people of Colour, disabled people, the poor, lesbians, religious communities, people identified with "controversial" genes: bring these groups to the table by asking what they want and taking their suggestions seriously; give assurance of not proceeding without them; give them power; accommodate their needs and voice; for example, Aboriginal women's groups will likely want representation from each of the three main Aboriginal groups before participating; some groups prefer to send two representatives; community groups may have suggestions as to how to structure workshop in a format conducive to community, not just academic participation.

 •For more established political groups, you have to "sell" the relevance of your chosen platform and objectives—be clear that they are of political relevance and will be a political force.

 •Keep an endless list of contacts and stay in touch throughout planning process to maintain good working relations and ensure commitment. In other words, inclusivity is important even in the planning stages.

Communication and Preparatory Materials

Establishing and maintaining communications prior to workshop is important for inclusion, to communicate goals and maintain group focus and to prepare for longer-term networking. Some suggestions:

Listserv and e-mail communications prior to and after workshop:
•Must be actively managed and focused.
•Be clear about who can be on listserv—recommended that it be exclusive to conference participants and issue at hand.
•Web page prior to and after, in order to facilitate exchange of information and research (from participants and organizers), publish updates and newsletters, and provide for public access/education (if resources for e-mail/webpages, etc. are not already on hand, check out the local university or community college Computer Program or Information Systems for potential students looking for placements or job training).

 •Use "Last updated" and "New" as tags so that browsers do not have to go through old material each time they log on for updates.

 •Keep it simple (i.e. avoid a lot of pictures, or have them optional or on links for downloading) so that loading website is quicker and more accessible by all software/ hardware configurations.

- •Be aware of issue of accessibility of a web page—who can access it and who can't?
- •Computer conferencing can be a useful model for ongoing communication. For example, there is a "Webnet" company in Toronto that will set up this ongoing exchange for groups.

•Newsletter—reports from Centres of Excellence, participant updates, etc. (may be circulated on listserv or posted to web page).

Mailings to participants—preparatory materials:

- •Official Invitation (mail as soon as the workshop date and participant list confirmed).
- •Participant directory—a list of contact information, who does what (include workshop organizers on list); if networking before workshop is desired, this list should be sent as soon as it is confirmed. Otherwise (or additionally) a finalised list can be distributed at the workshop.
- •A statement of goals/objectives for the workshop must be clearly articulated; include a list of what is expected of participants so that they will be adequately prepared; disclose any concerns, anticipated tensions/difficulties. In terms of expectations, it is appropriate to provide guidelines outlining how the participants should prepare for the workshop. For example, list questions that will help participants identify and frame the issue in their own terms. It is fair, and far more effective/efficient time-wise, to expect participants wishing to have a voice on the issue to have their position and concerns formulated in advance. If participants are not prepared to do their own homework beforehand, they can not expect to have a voice at the table. However, if lack of resources/funding is preventing groups from having a forum for identification of their own concerns, perhaps the provision of funding for their own internal (even a one day, on-site) preparatory workshop is necessary. This might be especially relevant for community groups who do not have the same access to resources as academics. Providing them with resources to do their own work before sitting around a table with academics and other groups may help to address issues of inequality and privilege which often arise in community-academic work (when seeking external funding, it is possible to request funding specifically for groups to meet or to hire writers for pre-workshop preparation).
- •"Issue-related" material, discussion papers, proposed models, samples of similar groups'/ conferences' recommendations. You may wish to have some feedback on papers by commentators before workshop—this will affect the timing of the mail-out and may be facilitated by a listserv or webpage (here again, recognise that not all participants may have access to this medium). It is important to have some select discussion papers in order to work from "common ground." Select brief yet detailed papers that highlight, summarise and raise specific issues for focus.
- •Agenda should be received at least ten days in advance.
- •Do not assume that all materials will be read by participants, however in pre-workshop communication, strongly encourage participants to do their reading. This is one reason for having a facilitator/informant present, i.e. to help fill in knowledge gaps. (See Section II, 1) Facilitation for discussion of informant role.)
- •Not all materials have to be circulated in advance. Material can be displayed on site, i.e. books, educational materials, video tapes.
- •Keep it simple—do not over-do amount of prep work required. Also, all documents and materials should be available in plain, accessible language.

Timing

It is difficult to establish a blanket timeframe for the preparation of a workshop, as the timeframe is dependent on a variety of factors such as available human resources, availability and accessibility of participants, level of experience on-hand, momentum already in place, and the capacity to draw on already-established resources/contacts. Given that workshops of relevance to the scope of the WGWNG's plans tend to rely heavily on part-time and volunteer work, and involve a diversity of cross-sectoral and nation-wide participants, a planning timeline of 9-12 months would be recommended. The two months just prior to the workshop are the most intense. Recognise that more work/time will be invested in the workshop than anticipated. It is also recommended that until funding is secured, no finalised decisions should be made, as an unexpected reduction in funding would mean having to repeat much of the planning process to accommodate for the gap in financing. However, establishing objectives and setting a tentative workshop date, timeline and preliminary participant list should be done as soon as possible.

II. Workshop Structure

The agenda needs to be both well focussed to keep the workshop activities on track and flexible to accommodate the group dynamic. Specifically, each item (or question requiring response) should have a goal listed beside it (i.e. to inform, to discuss, to decide) and a tentative time allotment. Workshop structure should reflect and facilitate the objectives outlined earlier on in the planning process. As workshop objectives will vary, the choice of a corresponding workshop format must be made on a case by case basis. A variety of options and suggestions are presented here, most conducive to a consultative and interactive format.

Facilitation

The use of a skilled *Facilitator/Mediator* is strongly recommended. It has been emphasised that "facilitator skills are not the equivalent of common sense. Rather, they are technical skills acquired through training and extended practice" (Silverman, 1986, p. 6). Specifically, a facilitator should be skilled at the following:

- interaction management (i.e. drawing out quiet members, identifying and mediating power dynamics, disagreement management);
- conflict management (understanding subject of conflict, personal conflict styles, strategies for management);
- group observation methods (how to step back from group to see what is occurring);
- maintenance of group focus and synthesis of group work. It is not effective to have the group set the agenda together, although some flexibility is necessary.

The facilitator should be a neutral third party in order to avoid biased facilitation. Her neutral status will also protect her from being the potential object of tension and anger, and will allow her to resolve disagreements that an involved party cannot. However, tension/conflict should not necessarily be viewed as negative, i.e. if everyone agrees about everything, you have to wonder if the necessary discussions and debates are taking place. Disclose tension/conflicts by allowing them to emerge so that they can be dealt with openly and in a constructive manner. Other key points:

•A head facilitator should be involved in the prep work for the conference, in order to be briefed about workshop content and goals, to learn about subject matter, to prepare for potential conflicts and opportunities, and to provide training to other facilitators. Other facilitators for small groups should be trained at an earlier workshop, preferably by the head facilitator. 3 facilitators are recommended for a group of 40 participants. The facilitators must make themselves available for consultation with organizers in advance of the workshop (to be briefed about workshop goals, potential conflicts, etc.).

•A periodic commentary/summary by facilitator during group work helps keep everyone on line and move group work forward.

•Facilitators should be capable of striking a balance between tasks (i.e. problem-solving, getting work done) and process (group interactive dynamics).

•She should have a working knowledge of subject matter, but not necessarily expertise: "Facilitators who are also experts in the substance of the project may get too involved in the technical details of the project instead of focussing on their essential climate-setting role" (Silverman, 1986, p. 12). She should, however, be prepared to provide opening comments and presentation of issues/information (about ten minutes) to group, as well as keep group informed throughout discussion/work and weed out things that are not pertinent to issue at hand. This is an "informant" role that may also be assumed by an individual other than the facilitator. However, in order to keep the process simple/clear, combining the facilitator/informant roles is advisable.

Informal Interaction

Informal socialising is very important to build networking. Do not over-structure agenda (i.e. leave gaps for socialising). Suggestions:

•have participants arrive early to socialise over snack/coffee before formal sessions start;

•arrange for entertainment (i.e. music, a social or cultural event, etc.) for evening, but be sure to make clear that attendance is optional;

•structure meals, snacks in a way that facilitates interaction—i.e. leave plenty of time, set out food/drinks in a contained area;

•leave some meals open to allow participants to make own plans and engage in their own form of socialising.

Formal Interaction

A *Keynote speaker* and/or *Chair* should open proceedings. She must:

•provide introductions (people want to know who is who);

•articulate conference objectives in a clear/focused way;

•outline agenda, instructions regarding facilities, etc.;

•frame issue well.

Each day's activities should be opened with welcoming remarks, some humour or other "light" discussion, followed by a summary of the previous day's work and the upcoming day's agenda. Similarly, each day's activities should be concluded with a review and participants should be given the opportunity to offer comments/feelings about the day's activities and offer suggestions.

In order to facilitate maximum participation between participants, formal speakers and presentations should punctuate rather than dominate the agenda, i.e. they should never be scheduled back-to-back. You do not simply want a presentation of papers and then discussion—this is too "academic." Instead, core activities should be small group work and discussion, preferably in a roundtable format. Suggested numbers for a working group are five to ten people. When dividing into small groups, decide whether or not you want all of the small groups working on the same themes, or whether each group will have a separate focus. One suggestion is to start the conference with small groups working on similar themes, in order to facilitate a common basis of understanding, and then move onto separate themes as momentum builds, in order to be more efficient with the time. Participants may offer suggestions and/or specify which particular theme they are interested in working with. When dividing participants into small groups, be aware of how each collection of individual participants might affect the proceedings in terms of working together constructively. Anticipate potential conflicts and the development of factions. Participants who know and are used to working with each other may leave others feeling left out with their "camaraderie." Also, group members who share similar backgrounds will tend to direct group work toward their shared modes and language or interaction.

The following suggestions are intended for small group work, however they are applicable generally to interactive group work:

- The role of facilitator/mediator/informant is key.
- Have a list/chart/overhead displayed at front of group that specifies the activities the group is to engage in, in order to maintain clarity and focus.
- Allow time for introductions.
- Have someone take notes in order to facilitate reporting back to larger group / plenary session; the facilitator may choose to do this on an overhead or flip chart so that participants can follow the progress of the discussion more easily. Another option is to assign a third-party note-taker to each small group who would work with the facilitator in synthesising group discussion for the plenary session.
- It might be useful to assign roles to participants within groups in order to encourage participation and a sense of ownership and responsibility towards the mediation/facilitation process. Roles may be assigned in advance of workshop if preparation is needed. Otherwise, they can be negotiated in small groups at workshop. Examples:
- Task roles ("critical thinker" roles): information seeker, information giver, critical evaluator, opinion giver, elaborator and summariser.
- Procedural roles: recorder, timekeeper, procedure developer, or progress evaluator; these roles help to keep the group on track and make all aware of the group process.
- May wish to keep speaker list.
- Effective interaction does not have to be "dry." The incorporation of brainstorming sessions, role plays and other alternative/creative formats might be equally effective and even provide needed breaks from discussion. In discussing an issue and potential action, it might be useful to refer to or simulate an example or case study. Engaging participants might also involve interactive written materials, for example, a workbook that lists questions and written exercises, with space provided for responses, in order to highlight key themes for workshop. It also provides a useful take-home exercise that the participant can use to work from for her own educational purposes.
- A constructive exercise is to attempt to frame action-oriented suggestions in a "to do" voice, rather than a "not to do" one, so that participants stay in a proactive mode.

•At the end of each session, allow each participant two minutes to speak without interruption.

Reporting back to the plenary session is important to maintain communication. The facilitator would be most effective at identifying key points. She may choose to present a synthesis of group work, referring back to notes made on an overhead or flipchart, and then providing the small group with the opportunity to make additions/corrections. The head facilitator or another individual may wish to, in turn, synthesise all of the small group reports onto an overhead or flipchart so that results are easier to review and are accessible to all participants.

At the end of the workshop, plan a wrap-up session where an attempt is made to draft recommendations and/or arrive at consensus where appropriate. The synthesis of small group reports will aid in this process. Before closing the workshop, allow every participant a "last word" without interruption.

Alternatively, the Consensus Development Conference of the National Institute of Health organizes an independent panel to observe workshop proceedings and synthesise material and issues raised. On the final day of the conference, the panel then circulates its recommendations for discussion. Conflicting recommendations are resolved and at the end of the conference a consensus statement is formally adopted. When consensus cannot be achieved, the statement reflects this by acknowledging uncertainties, options or minority viewpoints.

The workshop facilitator(s) and note-takers may be well-situated to synthesise the group work into a set of recommendations or consensus statement that would then be presented to the larger group for approval and comment. This role could also be assumed by one skilled individual who is knowledgeable about the subject matter.

Workshop Facilities: Physical Set-up

Ideally, the layout of tables should be in a "U" shape, so that participants can all see each other, make eye/facial contact, etc. The facilitator should work from the front of the "U" and avoid standing behind a table or similar barricade that might create a psychological and physical communication barrier. Small group work should take place in a similar arrangement, or around round tables. Visual aids, i.e. flip charts, overhead projector, are important cues for visual feedback.

III. Follow-up/Continuity of Networking

Have participants provide feedback. Suggestion: hand out an evaluation form at the beginning of the conference so that participants can make notes and evaluate the process while engaging in it. An executive report and conference summary should be forwarded to all participants. In addition, having a consensus statement or set of recommendations is useful in terms of facilitating networking and publicity. Such a document can be forwarded to government officials, healthcare associations/organizations, community groups, the media, journals, newspapers, newsletters and other targeted organizations and venues. Another option is to make audio and/or visual recordings of workshop proceedings available.

In addition to contacting participants on an individual basis for feedback and an assessment of their receptiveness to continued networking, the following modes of communication are encouraged:

•conference calls
•mailing lists

•listserv and e-mail communications
•web page
•follow-up workshops/meetings.
•use media effectively (i.e. media releases) to increase/maintain visibility of issue.

IV. Summary

In summary, I will start with a list of suggestions/comments made by informants who have had experience organising and holding similar workshops/conferences:

•Be sure that funding/resources are adequate for goals/size/scope of workshop.
•Assume it will take more work/time than anticipated to prepare .
•Be sure to stay within means and do not take on more than is feasible—if the organizers are burned out, there is not enough energy left over to continue work/networking.
•Challenge: it takes a lot of energy to keep up to date with issues.
•Have professional conference people organize it.
•Make use of skilled facilitators—pay good money if necessary, in order to get an experienced and neutral mediator.
•Choose participants based on how you know they will interact in the group—do not choose participants for optics.
•Clear guidelines about nature of discussion are needed in order to deal with potential conflict.
•Do surveys in advance to be sure the participants are on course with the conference objectives.
•Have a website up and running in advance to facilitate communication, exchange of information.
•Set up computer/internet conference on "Webnet" for organising—this is a very effective medium.
•Be sure that prep documents are not repetitious nor too time consuming and distribute them far enough in advance for participants to read them before workshop date.
•Have participants respond to prep materials/articles in advance of workshop (i.e. as commentators).
•Disclose tensions and possible criticisms beforehand so that participants are not surprised by attacks or unanticipated issues/tensions arising—i.e., be sure they all know what to expect.
•Give participants opportunity to meet "privately" before the public meetings/sessions start.
•Allow participants more time to meet as separate groups, organized around specific topics and special interests so that they can sort out their own views and then choose a spokesperson to present to the larger group.
•For small groups: allow each group member opportunity to speak and voice their position for two to three minutes uninterrupted and unchallenged, before debate opens up—moderator could then draw out specific issues that were raised.
•Videotape proceedings—this is useful for future work.
•Use media effectively (i.e. media releases).

It might be useful to point out that some of what you have read here appears to be contradictory. This is simply because I am attempting to account for and anticipate several sets of options that apply to differing workshop objectives. Rather than attempt to draw out any key points, I believe it will be more useful to provide a context within which to assess the report contents. On a simplified level, there are three stages to defining a strategy for action on an issue:

- grounding/identifying an issue by acknowledging its relevance, and sharing experience of the issue at hand;
- defining the issue by analysing its roots and subsequently identifying goals and objectives for dealing with the issue;
- developing the strategy, which includes identifying stakeholders, contemplating and deciding on a strategic approach, and anticipating results (Lewis and Barnsley, 1990).

Ideally, given adequate time, opportunity and resources, the first stage should already have been addressed by participants attending a strategic workshop. Otherwise, knowledge of the issue is not satisfactorily formulated to engage in strategic planning. On the other hand, stage 2) defining the issue, is more pertinent to a strategic workshop format. However, it only addresses the initial step in strategic planning, and would not be adequately complete if the final stage, 3) developing the strategy, is not reached. Deciding which level to intervene at, while facilitating group interaction and networking, is perhaps the most fundamental decision in terms of identifying objectives. In closing, I will emphasise that meeting the identified objectives requires, above all: focus, transparency/clarity of intent, and strong facilitation/mediation skills.

This report was written under the supervision of Lorna Weir, Ph.D., and Anne Rochon Ford, Community Co-Director of the National Network on Environments and Women's Health (NNEWH). It was made possible by Seed Grant funding provided by NNEWH and held by Principal Investigator Lorna Weir, Ph.D.

I wish to extend my thanks to the key interview participants/informants who generously offered their time, conference experiences and materials. They are: Becky Holmes, Lee Lakeman, Catherine Martell, Joan Meister, Ilana Mittman, Roxanne Mykitiuk, Marsha Saxton and Dorothy Wertz. Numerous others were also instrumental in providing me with resource materials and directing me to contacts. Their contributions are much appreciated.

Bibliography/Further Reading

Lewis, Debra J., and Jan Barnsley. (1990). *Strategies for change: From women's experience to a plan for action, a publication of the Women's Research Centre.* Vancouver: Press Gang.

Nadler, Leonard and Zeace Nadler. (1987): *The comprehensive guide to successful conferences and meetings.* San Francisco: Jossey-Bass Publishers.

Phillips, Gerald M. (Ed.). (1990). *Teaching how to work in groups.* Norwood, New Jersey: Ablex Publishing Corporation.

Roughton, Anne and Audrey Powers. (1979). *Workshop planning.* San Francisco: Bay Area Reference Center, San Francisco Public Library.

Schnexnaydre, Linda and Nancy Burns, et al. (1984). *Censorship: A guide for successful workshop planning.* Phoenix, Arizona: Oryx Press.

Silverman, Jerry M., Merlyn Kettering, et al. (1986). *Action-planning workshops for development management: Guidelines.* World Bank Technical Paper #56. Washington, D.C.: World Bank.

Smith, Ruth S. (1979). *Workshop planning.* 2nd ed., CSLA Guide No. 3. Byrn Mawr, PA: Church and Synagogue Library Association.

Conference Materials

"Canadian Biotechnology Strategy," roundtable discussion agenda and participant list.

"National Dialogue on Genetics," agenda and participant list.

National Institute of Health Consensus Development Program website: http\\www.consensus.nih.gov

"NRTs… The Contradictions of Choice: The Common Ground Between Disability Rights and Feminist Analyses," *Conference Summary Report.*

WAGICS conference website: www-unix.oit.umass.edu/~fholmes/

Women's Self Care Workshops
A Guide

PRODUCED BY THE WOMEN'S HEALTH NETWORK, NEWFOUNDLAND AND LABRADOR
WRITTEN BY KLAUDIA DMITRIENKO

This guide was developed by the Women's Health Network, Newfoundland and Labrador (WHNNL) after delivering a series of self care workshops across the province from September 2000 to February 2001. The WHNNL is a not-for-profit organization that works to improve women's health in the province by providing opportunities for networking and sharing information and by conducting and supporting research on women's health issues.

Self care involves being aware of our health needs and developing strategies for meeting them. As women, most of us learn to care for others very well, but caring for ourselves is often more difficult. The WHNNL wants to encourage women to be pro-active and to learn about and discuss issues that affect our health. It is our hope that groups of women throughout the province will be inspired to organize workshops or discussion groups that allow women to come together and share experiences, ideas and support around health issues relevant to themselves and their communities.

We at the WHNNL hope you and your group find these materials beneficial. We welcome your feedback and suggestions:

Women's Health Network, Newfoundland and Labrador, 12th Floor, Southcott Hall/Dr. L.A. Miller Centre, 100 Forest Rd., St. John's, NF, A1A 1E5, telephone: (709) 777-7435, fax: (709) 777-7434, email: whnmun@mun.ca).

How to Use this Guide

This guide provides a brief overview of how to organize and lead a women's self care workshop. It is designed for anyone who wants to discuss or learn about women's health with other women. Workshops may be held with any type of women's group in either a formal or informal setting. *You do not have to be a health expert* to do this. Ideas in this book can be used in a variety of situations by:

- women's self help groups
- women's social groups
- health educators
- both new and experienced group leaders
- women working with other women or girls.

At the WHNNL, we designed our self care workshops around the information and themes presented in our *Women's Self Care Book,* a resource guide produced to provide women in Newfoundland and Labrador with information and strategies to support and improve their health. You can use this book and other health resources (see page 25) to support discussions and answer questions that may be raised in your workshop. As a group leader, your role is to organize the event, provide some basic structure and facilitate discussion. You do not have to know everything about women's health.

Not every self care workshop will look the same. What you discuss will depend on the specific health realities of your community as well as the needs and interests of the women who attend. Use this guide as a resource for ideas, but feel free to incorporate your own activities and projects as well. Use the suggestions in this guide that are appropriate for you and your group.

Hosting a Self Care Workshop

Why?

Self care workshops challenge the notion that health issues should be left entirely to medical experts. Women need to take an active role in learning about and improving our health. We all have some knowledge and awareness of our own bodies, emotions and needs. Self care workshops/discussions provide an opportunity to help us further develop this knowledge.

As women, we are often brought up to put others first. Self care workshops aim to improve our sense of self worth and to encourage us to give priority to our own needs.

Sharing knowledge, feelings and experiences is important and can be a healing force in itself.

Too often women's health issues are seen as individual problems. Self care workshops encourage women to see their problems in the context of their entire lives and to draw out shared or collective solutions.

While significant advances have been made, women are still discriminated against in many areas of life. Providing a forum to discuss women's health concerns is a small step towards working to redress some of these inequities.

Self care workshops encourage an understanding of health that is holistic in nature. Women are encouraged to examine physical, emotional and mental aspects of their health and to examine the role of the environment, working conditions, social supports, etc. in determining their health.

Who?

Self care workshops are appropriate for any woman of any age. They can be held with pre-existing groups or can be widely advertised to bring together women who may not know each other. Although it is a good idea to have some experience working with groups, anyone can hold a self care workshop.

There are many active women's groups and organizations in Newfoundland and Labrador that could either host a self care workshop or provide participants for a self care workshop. Women's Institutes, women's centres, breast feeding clubs, new mother support groups, breast cancer support groups, youth organizations, church and other community service groups are only a few examples of women's organizations that exist in many communities throughout the province.

Ask around your community and you will likely find many women who are interested in the idea of a self care workshop.

What's Involved?

A self care workshop can be as formal or informal as you want. A workshop can last for two hours or an entire day. What it looks like will depend on the community and the facilitator. While some groups may wish to splurge on some extras for their gathering, *it is not necessary to have a lot of money or time to plan a self care workshop.*

The basic steps involved in planning a self care workshop are:

• general research into the issue you wish to discuss;
• developing a discussion outline with appropriate worksheets/resources;
• finding a venue;
• organizing childcare and refreshments if necessary;
• advertising the event.

The above steps will be discussed in detail in the next section. It is important to remember that the goal is to create a relaxed, enjoyable atmosphere where women feel comfortable sharing experiences, discussing differences and uncovering commonalities.

You may be nervous about leading a group discussion. Remember that you are not there as a medical expert or a therapist. A good facilitator knows enough about the subject to provide structure to the discussion and to encourage participation (this can be done through any number of activities / strategies) but you do not need to lecture. Everyone attending the workshop will have personal experiences and expertise to share.

Workshop Preparation

Good preparation helps ensure the success of your workshop.

Goals and Objectives

The first step in planning a workshop is deciding what are your goals. Do you want to hold a full day event that involves guest speakers and a video presentation or a very casual discussion for a few hours at your local women's drop-in centre? What you choose will depend on the resources available to you.

It is also good to think of what the general goals of the workshop are (no matter what its size). The following are some xamples of possible workshop goals:

• to bring women together to discuss pertinent health issues;
• to highlight the multifaceted nature of health;
• to emphasize the importance of self care;
• to encourage participants to look at their own health status/practices;
• to explore strategies to encourage self care.

Organizing

Once you know what kind of event you are aiming for, you can begin to organize. There are several basic items that you will need to address:

Venue: In what physical space will you have the workshop?
Women's centres, community centres, family centres, town halls, libraries and churches are all good places to find large, comfortable space available for community use (many of these organizations will provide their space free of charge). Hotel conference rooms are sometimes an option in larger

communities. If your planned group is small, an individual's home may work as well. It is important to remember the issue of accessibility for women with disabilities; ideally your venue will have ramps/ elevators (if there are stairs) and accessible washrooms.

Date/time: When will you have the workshop?

Women have different responsibilities that you need to take into consideration depending on the audience you wish to attract. For example, women who work outside of the home may only be available in the evenings or on weekends. Women with children in school may need to be home when school is finished. Women with young children may only be available later in the day when another family member is home to watch the children.

Refreshments: Will you serve food/drinks?

Providing some sort of refreshment is always a good idea. It also can serve as an example of (or a conversation starter for) healthy eating. If you do not have a lot of funds, local restaurants or grocers will often donate food when approached. Alternately, you could run the workshop as a brown-bag lunch session or as a potluck.

Childcare: Will it be available?

Some women may be unable to attend your workshop if childcare facilities or subsidies are not provided. However, it can be difficult and expensive to arrange for childcare at the location of the workshop. If possible, it is often easiest to let women know that funds are available to cover at least some of the costs of a babysitter. If this is not possible and / or your group does not mind interruptions, you can make a play area in one part of the room where you can all keep an eye on the children while you are talking.

Supplies

Self care workshops can be very low-tech. The only things you really need are a flip-chart (or big pieces of paper) and some markers. Additional items that you may want to have on hand are: pens, tape, index cards, paper, kleenex, etc.. If you wish to show a video, a television and VCR will be necessary. A tape or cd player for background music during breaks and small group work can also be a nice touch.

Finding Participants

Who you want to encourage to attend your workshop will be up to you. It is often easiest to work with a women's group that is already in existence. If you are just looking for a small group, you could just call up a few people that you know (asking them to bring a friend that you do not know is a way of introducing variety into the group). However, it is also possible to widely advertise throughout your community. Possible ways of advertising your workshop are: posters, announcements in community papers, announcements on your local cable tv, announcements in church bulletins, and by word of mouth. For a large event, it is a good idea to ask that people register. This does not mean they have to come, but it does give you an idea of how many people to expect.

Workshop Structure

Physical Space

The physical lay out of the room is often out of our control, but there are a few key point to keep in mind. If possible, set up the seating in a circle. Having everyone able to see each other encourages communication. Seating that is easy to move around is useful if you are going to incorporate small group work or role playing.

The temperature of the room can have a great impact on participants' energy levels (too warm makes people sleepy, too cold and it's difficult to concentrate).

Bringing in personal touches such as table clothes or a small throw-rug for the centre of the group can help to make a room warmer and more friendly. The idea is to create a comfortable atmosphere.

Facilitation

Depending on the size of your group or the length of your workshop, you may want to have more than one facilitator or group leader. Having more than one person lead the session and encourage conversation can keep things more interesting and help take the pressure off the other facilitator.

Remember to project your voice even if the room or your group is small. It is a good idea to check regularly with participants to be sure that you are speaking clearly and with enough volume.

It is always good to let the workshop participants know what the agenda will be for the session and to ask them if there is any specific information that they especially want to cover. As a facilitator or group leader it is also your job to set the ground rules for respect and confidentiality among participants. Discussing health can bring up very personal issues and experiences for many women. Everyone participating in the workshop needs to know and agree that information shared in the workshop will not be repeated outside of it.

Participants may be a little reluctant to speak up or be singled out in front of the group at first. Ice-breakers or warm-up activities can help people feel more comfortable (see page 12). After your ice-breaker (if you use one) it is a good idea to start with a general group discussion. Save activities such as role playing for closer to the end. Throughout the workshop it is the facilitator's job to judge how participants are feeling (do they seem tired, bored, uncomfortable or really interested in one area?) and to adjust topics or activities accordingly. You will need to be flexible with your plans. For example, sometimes it is best to allow women to continue exploring a topic even though the time you set for this has passed. Similarly, you may need to change topics or suggest a different activity if the current one does not seem to be engaging. The more groups you lead the easier "switching gears" will become.

Breaks

It is very important to set aside time for breaks in your workshop schedule. You should have some sort of break approximately every 45 minutes. These can take the form of a group stretch, a short relaxation exercise, a refreshment break or just a short "breather."

A short break like this should last only about 5-10 minutes. If your workshop is going on for several hours you will want to schedule longer breaks as well (for example two twenty minute breaks or a longer 45 minute break for a meal).

Below are two example texts, one for leading a group stretch and the other for a relaxation exercise. When leading stretches or exercise make sure not to do anything too strenuous for the members of your group.

•"Everyone sit up straight and bring your shoulders back as if you were trying to touch your shoulder blades together. We will hold this for a count of five. Make sure you are breathing. Now bring your shoulders to the front, and hold for five again."

•"Everyone stand up slowly. Breath in and sweep your arms up over your head. Stretch your arms towards the ceiling, spreading your fingers out wide and hold for a count of ten. Release down slowly."

Quick Relaxation Exercise

•Loosen your clothing and get comfortable.
•Tighten the muscles in your toes. Hold them for a count of ten. Relax your toes and enjoy the sensation of release from tension.
•Flex the muscles in your feet, hold for ten and release.
•Do the same moving slowly up through your body (through your legs, abs, back, neck, arms, face) contracting and relaxing the muscles as you go.
•Concentrate on breathing deeply and slowly.

Themes

Even if you are holding a general self care workshop, you may want to have some specific themes in mind to help direct discussion. You may also choose to focus the entire workshop on a specific aspect of women's health and self care. Some possible themes you may want to address are:

•women's wellness
•stress and mental well-being
•physical health
•knowing our bodies
•food, diet and healthy eating
•healthy lifestyles
•self-image/body-image
•the menstrual cycle/menopause
•sexuality and reproductive health
•relaxation/taking time for ourselves
•interacting with health care providers
•complementary health care
•women aging
•motherhood
•social issues that affect our health.

You could easily combine several of the above themes into a longer workshop or a series of workshops.

Strategies/Activities

There are many different ways of presenting information and encouraging discussion in a workshop. The ideas listed below are just a few. Feel free to adapt these ideas to suit your group or to develop new ways of creatively engaging women with health information.

Ice-Breakers

Ice-breaker exercises are designed to help participants get to know each other and begin to interact. They may or may not directly involve the health topic being discussed. There are innumerable ice-breakers and variations of ice-breakers. Three example are discussed below.

Paired introductions

Ask each participant to pair up with another participant whom they do not know (or someone they do not know very well). Each woman takes turns talking about themselves to their partner for a few minutes, making sure to include their name, a few interests, etc.. Once all partners have finished sharing information with each other they introduce each other to the group as a whole (e.g. "This is Mary, she lived in St. John's for many years but has moved back to Brigus for her retirement. She likes to garden and is very involved with her church group....."

Name game/cushion toss

Each participant thinks of a positive word to describe themselves that begins with the same letter as their first name (e.g. "Jolly Jane" or "Likeable Laura"). Everyone introduces themselves. The facilitator has a cushion or soft ball ready. The facilitator throws the cushion / ball to the first woman whose name she remembers (she says the name as she throws). That woman then throws the cushion to another woman whose name she remembers. Continue around the circle until everyone's name is remembered.

Belief statements

Before the workshop, the facilitator prepares cards (at least one for each participant) with different statements on them. These statements reflect certain beliefs or value statements about self care or a more specific women's health issue. Example statements are included in the box on the right. You can use these or think of similar statements. You can also think of belief statements for a specific topic (e.g. body image). Try to think of statements that make people think about how they feel. It is a good idea to include statements that encourage a strong agreement or disagreement as well as statements that are less black and white.

At the beginning of the workshop, all participants receive a card. Everyone stands up with their cards held in front of them, facing out. The women move amongst each other, introduce themselves and compare statements. For example, a woman would say, "Hello my name is .... and I do/do not believe [read the statement on the card]." The rules are that if you agree with someone else's statement more than you agree with your own you can take her card and give her yours (you have to give up your card if someone asks for it even if you do not like what you are getting in return). The goal is to try to end up with a statement you agree with.

Once everyone has been moving around for about ten minutes the leader asks that everyone return to their seats. The leader then asks for a show of hands as to who was left with a statement they did/did not agree with. The group can then discuss how they felt about the statements and why. Differing opinions are to be expected here—it is a good activity for examining the role of personal values in self care.

Here are some examples of health belief statements:

•Emotional stress affects my physical health.
•Reading about health issues is a waste of time because my doctor tells me everything I need to know.

Taking Time For Ourselves Worksheet

1. How much time do you have to yourself/to enjoy yourself:

In a typical day?_____

_____

During a typical week?_____

_____

2. If you do have time to yourself, how do you use it? What kind of things do you do to enjoy yourself/relax?

_____

_____

_____

_____

_____

3. What would you like to do if you had more time to yourself?

If I had ten minutes I would_____

_____

If I had an hour I would_____

_____

If I had a whole day I would_____

_____

Remember that taking time for yourself is an important part of your mental, physical and emotional well being!

Stress Worksheet

1. List your personal symptoms/signs of stress:

Physical_____

_____

Mental/Emotional_____

_____

2. What are some of the main causes of stress in your life?

_____

_____

_____

3. List those causes of stress that you would like to change.

_____

_____

_____

4. Choose one of your stress factors (it may be easier to start with a minor factor). What is the first thing you need to do to begin changing this factor?

_____

_____

_____

Worksheets adapted from Workers Educational Association/Health Education Authority, *Women and Health*, Manchester Free Press: Manchester, 1986.

- Eating well and being active are the best ways to stay healthy.
- I don't need to think about my health unless I am ill.
- Having friends is important to my health.
- Getting older means having more health problems.
- There is one body shape and size that is ideal for all women.
- Medical care is the most important factor in people's health.
- Most health information is too difficult to understand.
- Often we just have to accept ill health.
- Taking time for myself is good for my health.
- Women don't need to worry about things like heart attacks.
- Whether I am sick or healthy is out of my control.
- It is my own fault if I am not healthy.
- Where I live affects my health.
- It is often difficult to do all of the things you are supposed to do to stay healthy.
- I know what is best for my health.
- Good health is a result of good luck.

Group Discussion and Brainstorming

Group discussion is a natural method to use in a workshop setting. The group leader has an important role to play in drawing out responses from the group. Try to make sure everyone who has something to say gets to participate and that no one person dominates the conversation. It can sometimes be difficult to encourage participants to speak to each other / the group as a whole rather than just to the leader.

Brainstorming means putting a question or idea to the group and asking for their immediate response. People say their thoughts out loud and they are written down where everyone can see them (either on a flip-chart or blackboard or on index cards that can be posted on the wall). The resulting list of ideas can be useful as a basis for encouraging more detailed discussion or for sorting ideas into themes (if sorting is your goal, index cards work best as individual ideas can easily be moved around and grouped).

Paired Work or Small Group Work

Breaking into pairs or small groups can help to increase the involvement of individual women in the workshop. It also provides an opportunity to deal with sensitive issues which may be difficult to discuss in a larger group. Almost all of the activities undertaken in a workshop can be conducted in small groups (for example, surveys could be done in pairs or case studies examined in groups of 4). It is up to you to choose what format you feel is best.

It is sometimes useful to have additional space (or "breakout rooms") available for small group work. Otherwise you can assign each group an area of the room. It is quite common with paired or small group activities for a representative of the group to report back to the workshop group as a whole as to what was discussed. However, this report back is not always necessary (for example with activities where private stories may have been shared).

Questionnaires and Worksheets

Questionnaires, surveys and worksheets can be used both to encourage women to reflect on their own health status or beliefs and as a basis for group discussion. They are a very effective tool for self-appraisal and discussions of risk factors (e.g. a questionnaire asking questions regarding lifestyle factors such as smoking and exercise and nutrition habits). They require some preparation on the part of the group leader. You can find health questionnaires and worksheets in many resource books or you can design your own. The following page contains two examples of worksheets designed by the WHNNL to discuss stress in a self care workshop.

Case Studies

Case studies are an extremely useful workshop tool. Often health issues are too personal for women to feel comfortable discussing examples from their own lives. It can be less threatening to present a fictional or anonymous example for women to discuss. Case studies can provide an opening for women to identify with the health experiences of other women. They can then share their own experiences if they choose. Examples of case studies used in previous WHNNL workshops are included below, but leaders and groups can easily write their own. When writing a case study you generally want to depict situations that women can relate to. Case studies can be useful for getting women to think about women whose lives are different from theirs even when the health issue being presented is not a personal reality. It is a good idea to include guiding questions to encourage discussion. Case studies can be used for discussion in small or large groups. They can also be used as the basis for role plays.

Example Case Studies

Case Study 1

Emily is a recently divorced, single-mother who is returning to work to support her family. While she usually visits her doctor, Dr. White, once a year for a check-up, she has made two appointments in the last month because of severe headaches. Emily makes a third appointment and tells Dr. White that the headaches are still bothering her. Dr. White asks if the painkillers she prescribed the last time Emily was in had worked. Emily is too embarrassed to admit that she could not afford the prescription (she only works part time and does not have a drug plan) and just says "no, not really". Dr. White writes a different prescription and gives it to Emily. As in their previous appointments, Dr. White then asks Emily if there is anything going on in her life that is stressful that could be causing her headaches. Not wanting to waste the doctor's time with her personal problems, Emily does not tell Dr. White about the changes in her family and financial situation. She leaves the doctor's office hoping that this prescription won't cost as much as the last.

- •What is happening in this situation?
- •What do you find problematic about this interaction?
- •How did this interaction make Emily feel?
- •What could Emily have done to improve this experience?

Case Study 2

Karen is a university student in St. John's. She has always had problems with acne. She has heard that there is a medicine called accutane that can help and has made an appointment with her doctor, Dr. Grey, to ask about this option. When she sees Dr. Grey, he tells her that accutane is a good option for her. However, it is a serious drug that can cause birth defects if a woman is pregnant when she takes it. When Dr. Grey asks Karen if she is sexually active she looks a little embarrassed but says yes. Dr. Grey then says that it will be necessary for her to go on birth control if she wants to take accutane. Karen says that she would prefer not to; she does not feel it is necessary because she is a lesbian. Her only sexual relationship is with a long-term, monogamous, female partner. Dr. Grey looks a little surprised and says that he feels it would be best for her to take the birth control pill anyway. When Karen asks why, he says that it is "just in case". Karen does not feel that this is the right option for her, but feels that she has to agree anyway. The condition of her skin is really bothering her and she does not have time to make another appointment.

- •What is happening in this situation?
- •What do you find problematic about this interaction?
- •How did this interaction make Karen feel?
- •What could Karen have done to improve this experience?

Role Play

Role playing involves acting out a situation. It offers an alternative to discussion and help highlight issues and feelings in a creative way. Taking part in role plays can also help women overcome shyness and can be a useful tool for practising self care strategies. Role plays may deal with serious topics, but they are often one of the most humourous aspects of a workshop. Kids usually love role plays. Adults tend to be wary about "acting" at first, but generally enjoy the experience (they may require a little coaxing, although no one should be pushed to participate in a way that makes them uncomfortable). You should always have a second option on hand in case woman do not feel comfortable. For example, you might suggest that they read the situation to the group or treat it as a case study in a small group. Some women may simply want to observe.

As with case studies, you can role play real or imagined situations. They can be used to discuss almost any issues. The group leader can prepare a script or scenario for the role play in advance or the participants can design their own (this second option takes longer). At the end of a role play you should discuss the situation that was presented and how the participants feel about it.

The four example role plays below were used in previous WHNNL workshops with the following instructions:

Read the following scenario and discuss it in your group. Talk about how and why the person is or is not practicing self care. Create a short skit to represent this situation. Talk about how the person could do more to support her health needs. Create a different skit to represent a situation in which the woman is more effective in meeting her health needs.

Role Play 1:

Dorothy is going through menopause and has gone to her doctor to see about treating symptoms (hot flashes and moodiness). Her doctor strongly recommends Hormone Replacement Therapy (HRT). Dorothy asks if there is another option. She does not like taking medication in general, plus she thinks she has heard of possible negative health effects as a result of using HRT. Her doctor impatiently asks her where she heard that, says that HRT is the right thing and goes ahead and writes the prescription. Dorothy has her misgivings but begins taking HRT.

Role Play 2:

It's finally the weekend and Sue's husband has taken the kids out fishing for the day. This is the first

Women's Self Care Workshop Evaluation Form

Please indicate he best answer and/or answer in the space provided.

1. How interesting did you find the workshop?

❏ very interesting   ❏ somewhat interesting   ❏ not very interesting

What could have made the workshop more interesting?

_____

_____

2. How useful did you find the workshop?

❏ very useful   ❏ somewhat useful   ❏ not very useful

What could have made the workshop more useful?

_____

_____

3. What did you like best about the workshop?

_____

_____

4. What did you like least about the workshop?

_____

_____

5. Was the presenter:

   ❏ loud enough
   ❏ friendly
   ❏ organized
   ❏ easy to talk with

Thank you very much for your participation and your feedback!

day Sue has had to herself in ages. Unfortunately she has a list of chores that could keep her busy until Monday. Sue's friend Margie calls and says that some of the girls are meeting at her house for coffee, would Sue like to join them for a bit. Sue hasn't had time for a good chat in a while but says no because the ironing isn't finished. When John and the kids get back, the chores are done, but Sue is exhausted and has another one of her headaches.

Role Play 3:

Myra and John are both retired. After years of living in St. John's they have moved to a smaller community to enjoy a slower pace of life. While she is generally happy with her new home, Myra does miss her friends and her children who live in town. She has been feeling down for a while now and can't seem to shake it. She is also having trouble sleeping. She does not want to worry John and doesn't feel that she knows anyone else well enough to talk about these issues. Right now she is hoping that things will get better on their own.

Role Play 4:

Barbara is a 56 year old woman with cerebral palsy. She went for her first mammogram 6 years ago. At that time she had to have 8 x-rays taken of her right breast and 5 of her left (it was difficult to get a clean film because of her muscle spasms). The technician was impatient and Barbara was very uncomfortable. The experience was so unpleasant that she has not been back. She knows that breast screening is important, but does not know how to tell her doctor why she keeps missing the bi-annual mammogram appointments scheduled for her.

Closing Activities

It is sometimes difficult to stay on schedule, but it is a good idea to allow a few minutes at the end of the workshop for a wrap up and final comments. A quick overview of what you have done, such as revisiting the objectives laid out at the beginning of the day, is one way wrapping up the workshop. It is always nice to give the participants a final say as well. Going around the circle and having everyone state one important thing that they learned during the session is fairly standard. You can also ask participants to respond to questions such as "what ideas will you take with you from today," "what new health commitments would you like to make after today," or "what will you tell your family about today when you get home". Closing with a relaxation or meditation exercise is especially appropriate in a self care workshop.

Evaluation

While it may not always be necessary, providing an evaluation form at the end of a workshop can be very useful. It provides an opportunity for participants to anonymously tell you how valuable the experience was for them and allows you to improve the workshop for future sessions. The evaluation form provided on the following page is one used by WHNNL staff at the end of self care workshops.

Example Outlines

The following pages contain three example outlines (with presenter notes) of actual self care workshops conducted by WHNNL staff.

Example 1: Stress and Mental Well Being – A Women's Self Care Workshop

10:10 Introductions and Background (WHNNL, Self Care Project)
•Emphasize that we are not health experts.
•Our role is simply to facilitate, get people together and get them talking/sharing experiences.

Health and Well-being

10:15 Ice Breaker
•Circulate statements, who is left with something they do/do not agree with?

10:30 Brainstorm
•*Index cards*—write down one thing you do to stay healthy (post these—are people doing similar things?).
•Write down one thing you do to take care of yourself.
•What does this say about our understandings of "health" (holistic)?
•There are many aspects of "health" (physical, mental, emotional, spiritual) and we often are not balanced in the attention we give to different areas.

10:40 Whole Person Health Appraisal (divide into pairs, handout sheets)
•Goal of this exercise is to get us to think about the many different areas of health in our own lives and to help us identify where we currently are in terms of our health and well being (see sheet for instructions).

11: 00 stretch
•Seated: sit up straight, bring your shoulders back as if you were trying to touch your shoulder blades together, hold for a count of five – bring your shoulders to the front, hold for five.
•Standing: arch back, stretch arms and fingers out wide, hold for five to ten, let go.

Mental Well-being

11:05 Mental Well-being
•Important, often overlooked part of our health
•Dynamic state of being (we move along continuum), looks different for each person.
•Freud defined mental health as "the ability to work and play" – what do you think mental well-being means?
•Handout mental health checkup (answering yes to any of these may signal a need for change, problem-solving or getting help).

11:15
•In general, mentally healthy people have the capacity to feel things deeply, are willing to experience their feelings, are sensitive to feelings in themselves and others and appropriately express a wide range of feelings.
•A key part of mental well being is being able to recognize what we are feeling and why—this next group exercise is designed to encourage us to do this.
•*Feeling vignettes*—imagine how you might feel in the following situation: (write feeling words on the board) write down your five favourite and five least favourite feelings in small groups, come up with a top five list.
•You may want to try to be conscious of letting yourself experience these feelings more fully—try to be more open.

11:45 lunch

12:30 Stress Discussion
•What is it, how does it affect us? how do we experience it (physical and mental symptoms—when are these too much) How do we recognize stress in others? Do men and women experience stress differently?
•Stress worksheet (individual).
•Relaxation is key in coping with stress (headache demonstration/short relaxation).

Well-being Strategies and Challenges

1:15 Scenarios
•Groups skits/presentations.
•Discuss the challenges (time, money, knowledge, family commitments) and strategies (taking time, being easier on ourselves, etc.).
•Time for ourselves worksheet.

1:45 Wrap-up and Evaluation
•Emphasize the self care message.

****

Example 2: Self-Esteem and Body Image – A Women's Self Care Workshop

6:35 Background
•Give background on the WHNNL and the Self Care Project.
•Emphasize that we aim to provide space for women to talk about issues that affect our health (same sex group often helps to bring out some issues we might otherwise not discuss—want to foster connection and support among women).

6:40 Introductions
•Introduce yourself and say one thing that you do to take care of yourself.

6:45   Ice Breaker
•Body image beliefs (to get us thinking): Everyone gets a red card with a statement about body image. We all walk around and read other statements . If you agree with someone else's more than yours you take it. After five minutes, who is left with something they agree with? Who is left with something they don't? Why do you agree or disagree?

6:55   Discussion/brainstorm
•(Use flip-chart). Think of an example of a healthy young woman – what does she look/act/think like? Describe someone who you think is healthy and say why. Do the same for someone who is unhealthy (looking for behaviours and attitudes).
•Many of unhealthy habits may indicate eating disorders – define these and note we won't be focusing specifically on this.

7:05   Defining Body Image
•What does body image mean to you?
•Our definition involves how you see your body, how you feel about your body and how you think others perceive your body. Having a good body image means feeling positively in all of these areas
•Having a good body image is important because it is basis of health – affects how we feel about ourselves and how we interact with others. There is often a difference between our self image (how we see ourselves) and our ideal self image (how we want to be) = "image gap."

7:10   Body Image Continuum
•Defining attitudes and behaviours in terms of healthy and unhealthy is a little simplistic – body image and eating issues actually occur along a range/continuum. Generally people with higher self esteem fall towards the healthier end of the spectrum. Having a decline in self esteem can cause you to move down the range. We can be at different places along the continuum at different times in our lives.
•Place the following attitudes/behaviours on the continuum – explain why.

7:20   Activity
•Why is it challenging to have a healthy body image? – media, culture, gender stereotyping, competition, images, control
•Break into groups – look at ads and report back to entire group (what is the ad trying to say/sell, what is it saying about women?).
•Discuss: How does this stuff make us feel? How do people experience/express negative/low self esteem?

7:30   Snack Break

7:45   Talent Summary
•The majority of the negative influences on body image focus on what women look like – the next activity is designed to get us thinking about who we are inside and what we do as people.
•Everybody gets a talent summary sheet—form groups of 3.
•Round 1: taking turns, everyone names 2-3 internal qualities they have and says why (e.g., I am loyal because I stayed friends with Kate when everyone else decided she wasn't cool) (those

not talking write this down).

•Round 2: taking turns, everyone tells their group something good that they have done (those not talking write this down).

•Round 3: taking turns, one person sits while the others tell them what they know about them based on what they said earlier.

•In large group – what was the hardest part about doing this? (listening, bragging) Why is it difficult to think of/say positive things about ourselves?

8:15 Role play – Home, School, Community

•Identify some of the issues in your home/school/community that you feel create challenges to having high self-esteem and good body image—choose one issue—construct a role play to show how this happens and how it makes young women feel. Create a second skit showing what you can do to either cope with or change the situation.

•Debrief – what are the strategies you identified?

8:45   Wrap-up/Strategies

•Identify strategies for increasing self-esteem and improving our body image (being assertive, challenging others' comments/ideas, looking critically at media, focus on health—eating well and being active, recognizing your strengths, supporting and being respectful of others – especially those with differences, finding help or info if needed).

8:55   Evaluation

****

Example 3: Holistic Health and Self Care, A Women's Self Care Workshop

1:10   Welcome and Introductions
•Objectives: sharing experiences and strategies (not an info session).

1:15   Paired Interviews
•Name, fun, health issue.

1:30   Ice Breaker
•Health beliefs/values: who is left with a statement they agree with?

1:35   Discussion/Brainstorm
•What is health? What makes us healthy?

1:45   Define Holistic Health
•More than the absence of disease—physical, mental, social, emotional well-being
Good health allows us to use our abilities to the fullest, enjoy life and achieve goals—it is a resource for living.
•"Holistic health means taking account of the separate influences and their interactions." Draw diagram.

•Debrief: different dimensions of health (physical—concerns the body, mental—concerns the ability to think and make judgements, emotional—being able to recognize and appropriately express feelings)—all are important and all interrelated (how).
•What is "healthy" will differ for each individual.

1:55   Small Group Activity
•"Personal health practices": discuss and list the practices/attitudes that you currently have that support your health in each of these areas.

2:10   Debrief
•Are people doing things to promote their health? Do you think that there is more that you could do? What dimensions of health do we tend to neglect?

2:15   Role Play/Narrative
•Anna the Self Care Queen.

2:20   Debrief
•Why can't we all be like this? Would we want to? What are the barriers that prevent people from taking care of themselves?
•Access to info, money, time, poor services, other responsibilities / caregiving.
•Women take care of others very well but we often don't care for ourselves
•What does self care mean to you?
•Our definition of self-care: discuss—no matter what our limitations are, there are always things we can do to promote our health—often it is an issue of attitude—need to begin to value ourselves—we can't do everything, our own vision of self care takes place within the context of our own lives
•Self care may look different for each individual, but it often involves specific attitude (assertiveness, self-esteem), communication skills, personal health practices (nutrition, health checks, relaxation).

2:30   Break

2:50   Scenarios
•Act out skits on self care issues (break into 4 groups).

3:10
•Come back to main group, present skits.

3:25   Debrief
•Do you think they were realistic situations? what are some of the self care issues that are highlighted in these skits? What skills are valuable to self care? (assertiveness, knowing where to find health information, setting aside time for yourself, getting support from friends and family when needed, doing things just for fun).

4:00   Community Link
•While self care is an integral part of encouraging good health, it does not occur in a vacuum.

There are links between your ability to care for your health and the way in which society is structured (e.g. universal health care makes some things easier, but not when we don't have access).

•Discuss: beside ourselves, what resources do we have for encouraging good health? (health care system, doctor, library, community orgs., families, friends, outdoors, complementary practitioners).

•Caring for ourselves is made easier when we have good health services, healthy physical environments and supportive community structures.

•All of us belong to some sort of group, no matter how small, that helps to support health in our community. Think of a group that you belong to (family, social group, community org, health care system) and what that group does to support the health of community members (eg., policy, activity, rule, mandate – eg no smoking in the house, group that works to clean up city, works against poverty, etc.).

Think of a group you are involved in, find others involved in similar work/activities. Share with each other what it is that your group does that you feel helps support women's health.

•What areas do you think could be enhanced or improved in your community? What sort of groups/gatherings/organizations need to be formed or need to become more active?

4:20   Wrap-up

•Reiterate links between different dimensions of health (physical, mental, emotional) – must pay attention to all.

•Links between personal and community – need to pay attention to both.

•Revisit list of what we currently do to promote our own health. In the light of discussions, is there anything that you want to add to your list that you didn't think of before?

•Given the structure/constraints of your life, what could you be doing that you aren't?

•Sharing: volunteers to share something that they could begin doing to increase their level of self care.

•We hope we have suggested a useful framework for thinking about our health and ways we can support it. Hope that everyone is taking away with them at least one idea for something they may begin doing to support their own health and the health of other women in the community.

4:40   Evaluation

****

This guide was created with the assistance and support of many individuals. We would like to thank all of those who participated in the development and delivery of our Self Care Workshops as well as those who offered feedback for the development of this guide.

The Women's Health Network, Newfoundland and Labrador gratefully acknowledges the financial support received from the National Network on Environments and Women's Health (NNEWH), Research Grant, and the Government of Newfoundland and Labrador, Strategic Social Plan Demonstration Project Grant. NNEWH is financially supported by the Centres of Excellence for Women's Health Program, Women's Health Bureau, Health Canada. The views expressed herein do not necessarily represent the views of NNEWH, the official policy of Health Canada, or the Government of Newfoundland and Labrador.

Resources

This is only a small listing of some of the resources available to help plan a self care workshop. The WHNNL's Women's Self Care Book contains listings of additional resources and organizations (there are a large number of health related organizations in the province that can provide information and material for your use). Remember to consider the possibility of using films, television clips, written articles, or a guest speaker in your workshop.

Bibliography

The Boston Women's Health Book Collective. *The New Our Bodies Ourselves: A Book By And For Women*. Simon & Schuster: New York, 1992.

McDonnell and Valverde (eds.). _*The Healthsharing Book: Resources for Canadian Women*. Women's Press: Toronto, 1985.

Tubesing and Tubesing (eds.). *Structured Exercises in Wellness Promotion: A Handbook for Trainers, Educators, Group Leaders*. Whole Person Associates: Duluth, MN: 1994.

Women's Health Education Project of Newfoundland and Labrador. *Women's Resource Kit*.

Working Group on Women's Health. *A Profile of Women's Health in Newfoundland and Labrador*. Dept. of Health, Gov't of NF: St. John's, 1994.

Other

•Regional Departments of Health and Community Services
•Local community health nurses
•Well woman clinics
•Women's centres
•Newfoundland and Labrador Centre for Health Information
•Libraries

Sex Trade Advocacy and Research Workbook
Materials for Training Workshops with Community Partners

FRANCES M. SHAVER, DEPARTMENT OF SOCIOLOGY, CONCORDIA UNIVERSITY

Sociologists Dr. Jacqueline Lewis and Dr. Eleanor Maticka-Tyndale (University of Windsor) and Dr. Frances M. Shaver (Concordia University) have secured a SSHRC research grant to study Canadian public policy and the health and well-being of sex workers. Professor Leigh West (University of Windsor, Faculty of Law) is collaborating on the project. The overall goal of this research is to develop an understanding of the way public policies in the areas of health, social service, employment, policing, municipal regulations, and federal and immigration laws affect the health, safety, and well-being of sex workers. The study uses occupations in the sex industry for this purpose because a wide diversity of levels and types of policies affect the lives of sex workers; a current and growing body of research and commentary is available on health and safety factors related to sex work; and there are community organizations with frontline experience dealing with health and safety factors related to sex work.

It is expected that the three-year project will develop methods to examine a wide range of public policies from the perspective of their impact on health, safety and well-being. It will also provide in-depth information on how various policies affect sex work and develop guidelines to maximize health, safety and well-being in the sex trade. The project involves collaboration with a number of community partners, including the Regional Municipality of Peel Health Department, the Exotic Dancers' Alliance of Ontario, Stella of Montreal and the Sex Workers Alliance of Vancouver.

The Sex Trade Advocacy and Research (STAR) workshops were designed to extend the involvement of our community partners. Although actively involved since the project's inception and committed to providing in-kind support, the SSHRC budget did not include funds to hire and train the partners to be directly involved in the actual collection and processing of data. Given this oversight, we applied successfully to NNEWH for funds to hold a series of training workshops and to hire and train community members as research assistants. Excerpts from the *STAR Workbook* presented here include key interviewing and taping tips, the introduction and closure instructions for the actual interview, and the topics raised during the open-ended interviews.

Interviewing Tips

1. Preparation for the Interview

Know your guide

It is essential that you know the interview guide (I-guide) and practice reading the questions out loud before hand. The more knowledgeable you are about the questions, the more relaxed and natural you will be during the interview.

Ensure that you understand what the question is asking so you can probe for a full answer. Think about the probes you might use and the conditions under which they may be necessary (examples below in section 6: More Helpful Hints).

Contact potential respondents and gain permission to conduct an interview

This is a lengthy process that may involve pre-calls, introductory letters explaining the research goals in lay terms, and/or callbacks.

Be patient, polite, and accommodating at all times.

Keep in mind the points in the next section.

2. Authorization of Self, Study, and Tape Recorder

Presentation of Self

Be aware of how you are presenting yourself in the interview. How you dress, how you introduce yourself (will you affiliate yourself with a particular community group, as a researcher, as a current or former sex worker, all of the above, etc.) will likely make a difference. Be relaxed and friendly but not too casual.

Explain why the study is being conducted and what is expected of the person being interviewed.

Provide them will full information on how to reach you and the others responsible for the study.

Confidentiality

Reassure respondent that all the information they provide will be held in the strictest confidence.

Tape recorder

Ask for permission to tape the interview and explain why this is necessary. Point out that the tape will be destroyed or returned to them (whichever they prefer) after it has been transcribed.

Read the page of *taping tips* and follow the instructions.

It is permissible to turn off the tape recorder during the response to single questions. Take notes regarding the answer and do not forget to reactivate the tape recorder.

Remind them that you do not want names or identifying details of people, club owners, clubs, etc. If a name is mentioned, it will be removed in the transcript. Note the number on the tape counter when something like this occurs so it can be omitted from the transcription. If they are still uncomfortable with this, take the time to rewind the tape and record over the problematic section immediately.

If you cannot obtain permission to tape the interview the alternative is to take thorough notes instead.

3. During the Interview

Secure the environment

The interview will go more smoothly if both the interviewer and interviewee are comfortable (physically and psychologically). One way to alleviate some of the social distance between you and the interviewee is by offering to answer any questions they may wish to ask. For the most part, this exchange should take place at the end of the interview.

Be sure to settle in a quiet location where there is little chance of being disturbed by others.

I-Guide

Give the respondent a version of the I-guide to follow during the interview (a version excluding the detail on the probes is available). Remember to get it back at the end.

Ask Questions

Remember, your role is to listen rather than to talk. The interviewer should only be taking up 10% of the air-time.

Some questions may trigger emotions in either or both of you. If this happens a number of strategies are possible: simply wait quietly until the tears subside (silence is good), offer a tissue, suggest that you come back to the issue later in the interview, and/or ask whether they are ready to go on.

For more specific tips on how to handle questions see section 6 below (More helpful hints).

Take notes

Even if you are taping the interview, it is a good idea to take notes. It works as an interview aid (keeping you on track, helping you to formulate probes and approaches to upcoming questions). It also serves to build rapport with respondents since it provides a clear indication that you are interested in accurately recording what they are saying.

Even though note taking is much less threatening that a tape recorder, it is a good idea to ask if they mind.

Closure and exit

After completing the interview move toward closure by asking the following type of questions: Do you have questions about the interview? Are there questions or areas of information we have missed asking about? Is there any information you would like (about the law, policies, health centers, etc.)?

If you are unable to provide the requested information or to find it on the Referral Sheet, offer to telephone them later once you have found it. Alternatively, suggest they contact [put in the director's name or the key RA's name].

Remind them how to get in touch with you and thank them for their time.

Give them the honorarium and money for other expenses incurred (babysitting, transportation etc). Be sure to get receipts for the expenses.

4. Immediately After the Interview

Edit notes and record other details on the post-interview comment sheet

Include details on how it went, such as emotional aspects, interruptions, any resistance to questions, and your own personal feelings and/or observations.

Do a recording check

Listen to several sections of the tape to ensure that it recorded properly. If not, write up some notes on the missing information.

Do an internal consistency check

It is difficult to remember all of one's jobs and/or events in one's history. If you find inconsistencies in the respondent's recollection, most are there by accident (rather than design).

If you find any such inconsistencies or, indeed, any unclear areas of information, telephone the respondent and ask for clarification. Explain that we need an accurate record for the purpose of the research.

5. Final Steps

Return tape, notes etc. to the research office
Note: We should provide the name of a specific individual on the team to be the contact person.

Quality check of the interview
Another team member performs this check. The objective is to evaluate the quality of the interview and determine whether all answers are clear and have been fully probed. You may be too close to the situation, or have a blind spot—just because you know what the respondent means, does not mean anyone else does.

If areas are inadequately developed, you will be asked to fill in the details by contacting the respondent.

Note: The check also serves as a training tool by keeping you aware of your weaknesses, blind spots, any problematic questioning styles as well as your strengths.

Verification of transcription
When the interview has been transcribed, it is returned to you with the tape. You are expected to read it while listening to the tape to ensure that the transcription is accurate.

Ensure that any information the respondent did not want recorded has been removed.

6. More Helpful Hints

Avoid leading questions
Leading questions put words into the respondent's mouth.

DON'T: I guess you find this hard?
DO: How did that make you feel?

Note: The "DO" formulation allows the respondents to answer in their own words.
DON'T: Do you think we are spending too much on assistance to the poor?
DO: What do you think about the level of assistance to the poor?

Note: The "DO" formulation allows the respondents to answer in their own words.

Avoid loaded questions
Loaded questions encourage a particular answer.

DON'T: Should the mayor fix the pot-holed and dangerous streets in our city?
DO: What should the mayor do to keep the streets in top shape?
Note: The "DON'T" formulation is loaded for agreement (i.e., a YES answer).

DON'T: Should the mayor spend even more tax dollars to keep the streets in top shape?

DO: What should the major do to keep the streets in top shape?
Note: The "DON'T" formulation is loaded for disagreement (i.e. a NO answer).

Limit questions to those within the competence and knowledge of the respondent

POOR: How adequate are the services in your neighborhood?

Key agency informants may be able to handle such a question, but not members of the general population. If you ask such a question, be sure to remember that the respondent can only answer it with respect to his/her own experiences. Rephrase it in the following manner:

BETTER: What neighborhood services do you use? Are they adequate for your needs?

Clarify answers
Our goal is to obtain information. Probe for full answers by asking follow up questions such as:

What did you find difficult about that?
Can you give me an example?
I know what that means to me, but what does that mean to you?
You say you participate in X, but we'd like to know how often? (Probe for an answer linked to a specific time frame such as times in the last week or month or year.)

Note: Probes must be neutral and not affect the nature of the subsequent response.

Encourage respondents to talk
Our goal is to obtain full information; one-word answers are not useful. Tips to encourage fuller answers (especially when faced with a non-talkative respondent) include those suggested above under "Clarify Answers" and the following:

Use verbal clues: How is that? In what way? Does anything else come to mind?
Use silence (i.e., don't fill the empty space by talking yourself, just wait a little longer).
Non-verbal clues also help: tilt head, raise eyebrows, or make eye contact.

Record body language
Watch for and record body language when it is used to answer a question: a shrug, a nod or shake of the head. Body language does not record, so clarify and record what the respondent intends to convey. Keep notes with the question number or "speak" it in to the tape recorder (e.g.: respondent is nodding her head).

Note: Be aware of your own body language and how you respond to their answers: keep it non-judgmental.

Coping with interruptions
Ideally, the interview should take place in a location where interruptions (phone calls, children etc.) are unlikely. Often they happen anyway (e.g., you will interrupt the flow when changing the tape).
When returning to the I-guide, review the last thing they said:

You mentioned your sources of income were X, Y, Z. Do you have anything else to add?
You were telling me about the time you did X; do you have anything else to add?

Handling conflicting information and repetitious questions

Responses that seem to contradict earlier ones are usually inadvertent (rather than intentional) and tied to problems all of us may have in recalling details about their lives. (Can you rattle off your work history without thinking about it?) Use the following questioning style to clarify the issue:

Earlier I thought you said X, Y, Z. Did I misunderstand you?
It is important that we get accurate information, this answer sounds different from what you said earlier. Could you clarify the situation for me?

Note: This same strategy can be used when respondents mention that the questions seem repetitious.

Questions invoking tears or other strong emotions

Monitor your own and your respondent's comfort levels. If the situation becomes awkward or tense for yourself or the respondent, follow the suggestions for appropriate action provided below.

Interviewee: Listen to your respondent. If it appears that s/he is avoiding a question or that you have touched on a sensitive topic, take the time to decide how to proceed. If the situation becomes particularly tense, suggest taking a short break, or continuing on a different topic, or coming back to the topic later.

Watch the body language of the interviewee. This may give you an indication that they are getting uncomfortable. If you're unsure, ask. You may have misread the body language, or you may find the respondent is relieved to be given the opportunity to talk about their experiences and want to continue.

Keep your referral list at hand in case they want/need help (such as the address of a rape crisis centre, health clinic, women's shelter, etc.).

Interviewer: You are not immune to the situation and may well feel uncomfortable with a question or its answer. Give yourself time to recover (pause, check the tape, refer to the I-guide etc) and then continue with the interview. Later on you may find it useful to debrief with another team member.

Always maintain open lines of communication with other team members and bring such issues to the team meetings for discussion.

Additional Interviewing Tips

1) Remember the goal of the research.

To find solutions to improve the health and safety of sex workers in their work environment. Remembering the research goal allows us to focus on certain issues, without giving the impression of overlooking other essential questions. Don't forget that the PI has already done some work in the field and has gathered certain information. This may be why you feel like you are not asking the right questions. On the other hand, it is important to collect information that you feel is important, that will enrich the data collected while remaining within the scope of the project.

2) Ice Breakers.

Arrange to meet the interviewee at the corner café. If appropriate, have a coffee and smoke a couple of cigarettes (the majority of the respondents are smokers). This gives you a great opportunity to create a rapport with the interviewee by talking about whatever you like, or, you may choose to discuss the project and answer any questions they have. After about 15-20 minutes, or whenever the respondent is ready, proceed to the interview room, and begin the interview. (You may want to let the participant choose whether he would like to take a couple minutes to have coffee and a cigarette, as some may wish to get started immediately.)

3) Ask questions as if it were a normal conversation.

When you are able to do so, skip from topic to topic, following the natural flow of the discussion but staying within the parameters of the interview guide. Glance at your interview guide when you feel you have asked all your questions, this will allow you to check whether any questions have been missed. Let your interviewee know what you are doing: looking over the guide to make sure you haven't missed anything. This also serves to make the informant aware that s/he is crucial to the interview process. It also helps to eliminate the possibility of repetitive questions.

4) It's up to you to properly formulate your questions.

Adapt your language to the respondent's language level. If necessary simplify your questions or add to them by including examples when the informant does not seem to understand the question. Ask the director if you are unsure about the meaning of a question. If you do not understand an informant's answer, ask them to clarify their answer and encourage them to provide examples.

5) It is best not to interrupt an interview for a coffee break or for any other reason.

To date, any break in the interview has had a negative effect on the process. Often, the second half was difficult because the respondent was tired and less open to questions.

6) Use the silences.

Count to ten in your head after each question. This gives the respondents time to think and to add anything they would like. It's not easy and requires discipline. If you feel a certain unease, ask yourself whether it is really the respondent who feels uneasy or yourself. Try not to respond to questions with non-verbal communication: the recorder will not pick it up.

7) The university office interview locales are not "cool."

The interview locales may not be "cool"but they are the most practical. They allow us to easily monitor the interviews, both on a personal and technical level, and to verify whether this person is here for the first time, or is trying to participate a second time. In addition they provide a quiet, confidential environment for the tape recorder. It is a good idea to avoid places where illegal activities may be in progress (bawdy houses, etc.).

8) Don't stop taping until the interviewee has left the room.

The respondent may say something very important once the interview is officially over.

9) Each interviewee decides to participate in the research for specific reasons.

Each interviewee decides to participate in the research for specific reasons that may not necessarily be in agreement with our own motives. This is a normal part of the research process. You will, therefore, have to negotiate between these two positions in a way that allows us to get the most information, while protecting the interviewee.

10) Don't forget about "outreach."

Encourage/invite the interviewee to talk about the project to people they know. We are in need of dancers, escorts and masseuses. Without them we will not be able to complete the study.

11) Ensure that the respondent signs the receipt.

12) Only one interview a day.
    Since doing an interview is very demanding, do not do more than one a day. In addition, give yourself enough time after the interview to complete your notes. Make sure you have enough energy to finish the interview without getting too tired.

13) It is important to talk about any difficulties experienced during the interview.
    Some people may have experienced some really difficult, even horrifying things that they share with you. After an interview you may feel heavy, sad, frustrated or you may simply feel the need to talk. Don't hesitate to call or e-mail us! If you can't contact another interviewer, write it up in your journal! You will feel better afterwards.

14) Once the respondent has left the interview room:
    It is important to ensure the quality of the interview, and to rewind the tape to the beginning of the interview. Make sure that the tapes are labelled properly and that the forms are filled out (cover page and post-interview comments).

Interview Taping Techniques

    1. Always use fresh batteries (alkaline NOT rechargeable) and tapes for each interview. Once batteries have been used for an interview, you can keep them for your walkmans, etc.

    2. Always take extra fresh batteries to each interview.

    3. Always take more tapes than you think you will need to each interview.

    4. Always put batteries and a tape into the recorder and check the recorder before heading to an interview.

    5. Be sure to set the tape speed to 2.4 . This provides 30 minutes per side and allows for a higher quality recording than if set at 1.2 (which gives 60 min/side).

    6. Set counter to zero (0).

    7. Be sure to check the volume setting before starting an interview. To ensure good sound quality, the volume control should be set 2/3 of the way to maximum.

    8. *Never* use the voice-activation setting on the tape recorder.

    9. Most tape recorders do not notify you when the tape runs out. Therefore you must find a way to keep track of this. One suggestion is to check your watch when starting the recorder and place your watch so that the face is visible to you. You should also warn the interviewee that you may have to check your watch every now and again to make sure the tape doesn't run out.

10. When the interview is finished, be sure to label each tape. Include your name, the interview number, and the number of tapes (e.g., 1 of 2).

Topics for Interviewing Sex Workers

The Introduction and Closure instructions are included here along with the topics raised during our open-ended interviews with sex workers from several sectors (street prostitution, escorting, exotic dancing, massage).

Introduction

What we are going to be doing in this interview is talk about your work. What I am especially interested in is how your work is affected by the way the police, social services and the city operates. I am also interested in some of the issues you may have around staying safe and staying out of danger (physical, emotional, legal) and how staying safe could be made easier. At the end of the interview you'll be paid $35 for helping us with this project.

I have a copy of the questions I will be asking that you so that you can look at as we go along [give copy].

You are free to refuse to answer any question I ask, or to withdraw your consent to participate in the study at any point during the interview. All information provided during the interview will be kept confidential. As explained to you on the telephone, I will be taping the interview in order to ensure we correctly recorded what you have said. Is that okay with you?
Once we finish the interview a transcriber will be typing up what we have said. She will remove any names or personal references as she does the typing. Once the interview is typed we can either return the tape to you or we will destroy it. This will ensure that there is no way to connect anything you have said to you or anyone else.

Before we get started I was wondering if there are any questions you would like to ask.

Topics Covered

Basic Demographics
Work History / Work Experience(s)
Advantages / Disadvantages of work environment(s)
Health and Safety Issues
Health Care (concerns and access)
Drug Use / Issues (medical and non-medical, alcohol, treatment)
Knowledge of / Experience with laws, by-laws, courts, police, diversion programs
Knowledge of / Access to / Use of agencies, social services
Making Work Safer (What others can do. What you do.)

Closure

Thank the respondents for their participation in the project and pay them the honorarium ($35).

Reimburse any other expenses incurred and ensure that the receipt is signed.

Get permission to telephone them at a later date if we need to clarify any of their answers after reviewing the recording. At the same time, determine whether they want the tape cassette returned to them once it has been transcribed, or simply destroyed. Assure them once again that the information is confidential and that all demographic information linking them to the transcription will be destroyed.

If they appear interested, invite them to participate in the recruitment of other participants; provide them with STAR matches and flyers if they agree to do so.

They may keep the sheet describing the project for future reference. In addition, give them the business card of the project director to keep as well.

Be sure to have them return the short version of the Interview Guide before leaving the interview.

As soon as possible after the interview is completed:

(i) verify that the sound is good on the cassette;
(ii) complete the Post-Interview Comment Sheet;
(iii) return the recorder, etc. to the project director.

Education for a Healthy Future

Training Trainers for Primary Prevention:
Participatory Action Research and Evaluation (PARE) Project

DOROTHY GOLDIN ROSENBERG, WOMEN'S HEALTHY ENVIRONMENTS NETWORK

This WNH&E-PARE project promotes awareness, education, and advocacy on suspected environmental links to breast cancer and other reproductive cancers and related conditions in the context of environmental mutagens, carcinogens, hormone disruptors, electro-magnetic fields, etc.

The Project supports goals of empowerment and the deepening of knowledge on *primary prevention,* the *precautionary principle,* and *environmental sustainability* by promoting capacity building through hands-on Training Trainers workshops and the production of useful and relevant materials.

CCWED, MNEJ and WABA collaborated to develop resources on environmental knowledge and environmental health relationships. These resources are being used in personal and advocacy activities. Mobilization has resulted in increased awareness and action.

Project Support

WNH&E received funding from the National Network on Environments and Women's Health (NNEWH), York University; the Saunders-Matthey Foundation for Breast Cancer Research, Ottawa; and the Canadian Breast Cancer Foundation (Ontario Chapter)—with appreciation for their support for this valuable program.

Background

Despite the fact that information about women's health is available from a myriad of sources, e.g. media, science, government, medicine, relatively little serious attention is paid to the physical environment's impact on our health. Often, when environmental toxins are discussed, they are marginalized as "unproven" threats and dismissed. However, with the rise in breast cancer incidence, immune system deficiencies, reproductive failures, birth defects, developmental problems, and other conditions, many women are joining in an international movement to focus on pollution prevention as perhaps one of the most overlooked keys to good health!

WNH&E was founded in 1994 in recognition of the need for policy and action in the face of scientific uncertainty. It promotes a holistic approach to women's health and recognizes other health models besides the current biomedical approaches. A major WNH&E goal is to build and strengthen knowledge through reflection and action in this widest sense by helping to shift the cultural medical paradigm from "magic bullet cures" to include more holistic and complementary approaches to health promotion including primary prevention. Another goal is to help groups in communities, social, cultural, workplace or policy contexts to develop tools and programs to broaden knowledge, build skills and improve confidence. This is often necessary in order to integrate environmental health issues into their ongoing work. Since its inception, WNH&E has been facilitating the development of resources and strategies for learning and change—locally, nationally, and internationally.

Concepts of primary prevention promoted by the International Joint Commission on the Great Lakes (IJC) include the "Precautionary Principle" and "Weight of Evidence" – meaning where there is suspicion of harm (rather than the demand of absolute proof of a particular substance causing a specific disease), that activity should be stopped. The IJC also calls for "Reverse Onus" which demands proof that a process or substance be safe *before* it is permitted – not afterwards, as is currently the case. There are safe alternatives to most toxic products and most toxic processes, which must now be promoted.

The film *"EXPOSURE: Environmental Links to Breast Cancer"* and its accompanying guide *"Taking Action for a Healthy Future"* were created as catalysts to raise awareness of the connections between health and the environment. Issues addressed include: chlorine, mammography, pesticides, plastics, radiation, tamoxifen, the medicalization of prevention, and the need for prevention advocacy.

Following the release of the film in 1997, women (and many men) questioned: What could they do on both a personal level and in the wider communities in which they lived and worked? Why they did not learn more about primary prevention from doctors and other health professionals? And, what they might do to push research and public policy agendas in the direction of primary prevention? As we began to use the film and guide in diverse situations, the need for more intensive 'hands on' use of resources was evident. In response to that need, Training Trainers Workshops were created for those who were interested in guiding their own communities, groups, colleagues, friends, physicians, and government representatives to develop and integrate environmental health literacy into all aspects of living.

Training Trainers Workshops are designed for a wide variety of groups with a wide variety of needs— women's, health, anti-racism, disabled, and community. The workshops, which include popular and adult educational processes are important, especially for those for whom the issues are new and/or are inexperienced in leading groups themselves. During the workshops, participants familiarize themselves with the issues and apply them in role-playing scenarios such as those they might encounter. This approach helps to develop knowledge, skills and confidence. They are urged to identify problems and barriers, examine leadership and community involvement, and develop strategies according to their needs. At the conclusion of each workshop, participants evaluate their accomplishments by reviewing their pre-defined needs and goals. Thus far, eighteen workshops have been held, three of which are the substance of this project and this report.

Participatory Action Research

Participatory Action Research involves a sharing of knowledge, power, and skills in the research process which changes and builds as participants define research questions, shape the process, and interpret findings in collaboration with researchers. Participatory Action Research appears to have several potential advantages over traditional research approaches. Most often, researchers have stayed at arm's length and have maintained control of the research process. Participatory Research calls for the *active* participation of those who will most benefit from the research. Concerns of power and justice are central to the process which is biased in favour of those otherwise left out of the decision-making process. In the case of environmental health concerns, this can include women in breast cancer, health, environmental, and community groups as well as independent scientists and health professionals who challenge current biomedical technological-only approaches.

In Participatory Action Research, participants are engaged in the whole process starting with their knowledge of the issues, the role they can plan (acknowledging their own realities), their understanding of how power relationships work through to the potential for communication and action with others engaged in the issues. In all workshops, approaches to learning are based on participants' needs. Activities may include community meetings, focus groups, video documentaries, community drama, art, etc., which contribute to awareness. The resulting research is then used as a framework for action.

This PARE (Participatory Action Research and Evaluation) process combines research, education, action and evaluation through community-based investigation for both personal and structural transformation on health. The Workshops were designed with members of the collaborating groups developing the questions, identifying problems and barriers, examining leadership and community involvement, and developing strategies and activities appropriate for their unique communities. An important outcome was a guide, which was produced for educational, community, professional, and policy advocacy specific for each partner.

PARE Partners

WHN&E identified three groups with diverse perspectives for the project: The Multi-racial Network for Environmental Justice (MNEJ), the Canadian Centre for Women's Education and Development (CCWED) and the World Alliance for Breast Feeding Action (WABA).

The Multi-racial Network on Environmental Justice (MNEJ–flyer 1995) works from ethnoracial perspectives to facilitate learning from environmental health and environmental justice perspectives – defined as "*an intersection of social, political, economic, health, and environmental relationships.*" Environmental justice recognizes that all humans from all ethnic and economic backgrounds have rights to live and fully participate in healthy communities. It encompasses the struggles of the workers, women, and people of colour who face an unequal share of Canada's environmental degradation. MNEJ creates a new agenda for social change.

The Canadian Centre for Women's Education and Development (CCWED) is comprised mostly of new immigrants, low-income women on social assistance, and youth in Scarborough (Toronto) and area. For many, the practical realities around access to health services, environmental information and safe products may be very limited. However, they are people of diverse racial and ethnic backgrounds whose knowledge may yield unique ideas from which we all can learn. CCWED's health promotion work consists of healthy eating education, pre and postnatal health services, counselling and support in immigration, and other legal matters such as divorce.

The environmental justice perspectives of MNEJ and CCWED comprised of members from diverse countries of origin provided an opportunity for the integration of health issues to reach a wider audience in a more suitable perspective, according to participants.

The World Alliance for Breast Feeding Action (WABA) offered a new direction in our prevention work relating to contaminants in breast milk and action needed on local and global levels to combat this situation. WABA includes a network of breast-feeding activists, mothers, health professionals, academics, and women's health groups. WABA provides links to literature, resources, and local and global initiatives, and is engaged in the promotion of breast-feeding and the concerns of how environmental threats affect breast-feeding mothers and infants.

Program Framework

Active Involvement of Diverse Communities

Sixty percent of the research involved members of marginalized groups such as new immigrant, low income, dis/abled, and diverse cultural communities.

Community Cooperation

COMMUNITIES COOPERATIVELY DEFINING THE RESEARCH:

- What was the prior knowledge of issues?

- How did participants define the issues?

- What were the barriers to accessing information and working on the issues?

- What sources of information did participants have access to and/or use?

- How did personal learning styles affect the communication of information?

- What did participants learn?

- What was lacking?

- How could participants incorporate the learning into their existing lives, work, and community involvements and what were their needs to do so?

- What steps would address issues and how could participants take action?

Action Plan

The workshops were planned and organized with the partners. MNEJ and CCWED are grouped together in this report because of their common focus of race, class, gender, and ableism and marginalization. Both MNEJ and CCWED organized their members for participation in the workshops and in the follow-up stages of the research. The feedback was useful in the development of guidelines appropriate for immigrant, low income, and marginalized groups. The suggested ideas can help communities create workshops appropriate to their needs for school, community, cultural, spiritual, workplace, professional, practical, and policy education and advocacy on environmental health.

While the term "environmental health" per se was new for many in the CCWED, there was a common knowledge that cancer, asthma, allergies, and the like were related to chemicals, water, food, poor air quality, etc. This workshop of new immigrant, low income, office and community workers, and youth addressed the issues—some for the first time—in novel and practical ways and included environmental primary prevention in their health promotion activities.

Prior to this session, most thought that they did not know much about environmental health issues. They wanted to become familiar with environmental health issues in an ethnocultural context, develop environmental literacy, and better integrate the learning into their lives and work. According to the coordinator, "This workshop really opened up their eyes. It has changed their world." They have all begun to take action.

Participants of the MNEJ workshop included students, office and community workers, educators, health practitioners, policy advocates, facilitators who work with immigrants, refugees, various cultural groups, women's health centres, students, anti-racism groups, etc. and similar to CCWED participants, wanted to become more familiar with environmental health issues in an ethnocultural context, develop environmental literacy, and better integrate the learning into their lives and work. Both MNEJ and CCWED highlighted issues of diversity, social location, equality and environmental justice, race, class, dis/ability, culture, age, sexuality, health, language, gender, workplace, community, power relationships, frequent isolation from mainstream activities and resources, and the need for jobs and other economic considerations. CCWED in particular stressed the concerns and problems of youth. CCWED also identified potential audiences for workshops such as schools, cultural and community organizer groups, community economic development, new immigrant, ethnoracial groups, etc. Both groups felt that these workshops were relevant because many in cultural communities are unaware of environmental issues and/or the resources available for raising their awareness.

Goals, Objectives, Needs

Similar goals, objectives, needs of CCWED and MNEJ—all within a cultural, equality, anti-racism and dis/ability framework:

1. To become familiar with and obtain a basic understanding of overall environmental issues, particularly within an environmental health and environmental justice framework.

2. To learn specific information on the common causes of breast and other cancers, environmentally linked diseases i.e., asthma, allergies, environmental sensitivities, etc., and how to avoid them.

3. To practice environmentally safe and friendly ways to wash, prepare, cook, and eat food and to educate family and friends about these things.

4. To learn more about complementary ways of healing (ways that are not usually presented by the medical profession), gain access to new information, and confirm traditional/cultural ways of knowing about health.

5. To discuss relevant issues not normally talked about in society.

6. To encourage community leadership, develop political organizing skills and strategies for addressing these environmental health concerns with decision-makers.

Participants raised the need for access to information and resources now widely available in the Toronto area and in most major centres, from environmental groups, newspapers, journals and the media, and the Internet. However, many immigrants, refugees, and cultural communities feel isolated and unable to access this information. They need communications in Tamil, Hindu and other languages.

Learning Styles

Both groups emphasized that how people learn affects relationships to information. They highlighted: discussing and sharing experiences; learning together; learning by doing (experiential); using print literature; stories; plays; theatre; songs; dance; films and videos; tapes and sign language. They stressed the importance of applying the new knowledge so as not to forget it and that facilitators use simple language so that everyone can understand the discussion, especially when English is not a first language. They insisted that solutions to what people can do always be included in the workshops.

Processing information and educational tools for workshops included:

•Asking how to help make these concerns relevant to each cultural community by using participatory methods.

•Helping groups strategize and network together better in the future by addressing common needs and issues.

•Working with culturally specific groups in their own contexts; with younger and older generations.

•Including campaigns: to educate for safe products; to read labels on foods; to demand labeling of genetically modified foods; to obtain affordable organic food; to learn the dangers of using aluminum cookware; the problems of using plastic containers and saran wrap which leach nonyl phenol bisphenol A and pthalates into the food.

•Allowing sufficient time for input so that everyone's voice is heard and everyone's needs are met.

Barriers

Barriers to be overcome in accessing information and working on environmental health included language, lack of education, low-income exploitation, (i.e. cheap aluminum cookware), age, and other forms of marginalization. Barriers to incorporating the learning into schools, workplaces, communities, organizations, programs/activities, etc. include the need for other ways of communication and learning, such as sign language, tapes and videos, the lack of funding, and the lack of resources to produce materials in different language. (The Sierra Club now has materials available on pesticides, air pollution, climate change, biodiversity, and shrimp farming in Mandarin and Spanish but, presently, none exist for the needs of the South Asian communities).

Future Actions

Policy and Educational Concerns

Policy concerns included health and pesticides, food issues in general, air quality, radiation, housing, transportation, performance of corporations, cleaning and removing chemicals and toxic materials, cancer prevention, animal rights, federal health service, standardization of and acknowledgement of alternative and traditional systems, and access to and coverage for alternative health care.

People need to know more about: pesticide harm (stricter laws and enforcement are needed); paper waste and the need for recycling; using non-disposable dishes and cutlery rather than throwaways; using public transportation or biking when possible; avoiding fluoride toothpaste (or a small amount at a time); and the dangers of microwaves. Everywhere, children at an early age should be learning about caring for the Earth; families should learn about organic foods and how to access them cheaply (i.e., South Riverdale Community Health Centre, Toronto Food Policy Food Council, etc.); lobbying skills need to be developed in order to effect change; fact sheets need to be developed for supermarkets, libraries, and cultural groups with the translation of materials into different languages.

There is a need to develop responses to those who negate the impacts of environmental carcinogens and mutagens with "there's not enough evidence to be concerned with." Although thee is now an abundance of literature on these topics, it can come down to "my scientist vs. your scientist" so often the best response is to use the IJC recommendations of precautionary principle and reverse onus referred to earlier—if it cannot be proven safe, don't allow it in the environment. The fact that we are now exposed to so many toxic substances means that it is problematic to test for one substance at a time because we cannot know what the impacts of synergistic or antagonistic interactions taking place in our bodies may be.

However, there is much evidence that illustrates damage in wildlife animals, birds, and fish.

Values

Issues of inter-generational immigrant values worth noting here can be similar to those of immigrants in previous eras according to MNEJ. Often newcomers just want to "do well" and become successful consumers—like most North Americans—replete with cars, homes in the suburbs, wasteful lifestyles, and the like promoted by public relations and advertising. Of course there are also those who bring with them cultural and traditional values and practices that honour the earth, her resources, and health. Some second generation immigrants, because they have had more security, education, choices, and languages skills, have developed ecological knowledge and are challenging their families and communities to become more environmentally responsible.

Needs of Women in Different Cultural Contexts

Women working in particular cultural communities re-conceptualize issues when confronting health concerns. Strategizing around advocacy with breast cancer survivors (and those with other conditions) must be dealt with in a culturally sensitive manner. For example, a breast cancer survivor who works with South Asian and other cultural communities explained that women with cancer in those communities often ask themselves what they may have done in a past life to have brought this upon themselves. Another example is that promotion of Breast Self Exam (BSE) could be offensive to women in different cultural communities who do not feel it is appropriate to openly discuss issues around sexuality. These important learning experiences must be recognized as the realities of some women's lives and must be reflected in participatory approaches in working with them.

The WABA/WNH&E Program

The purpose of the WABA/WNH&E workshop on breastfeeding and toxins was to brainstorm about the difficult topic of breast-feeding and breast milk in a polluted environment. As noted, environmental toxins are found throughout the food chain and enter our bodies by many sources. It is a common notion that a mother's body is a child's first environment and that toxic substances in the mother's body are also in her milk. Of course, environmental pollution is not just a breastfeeding issue. It should be everyone's concern considering that in today's world, even prior to conception, the eggs and sperm are bathed in chemicals unknown to mammals several decades ago. The implications for future generations are cause for action for prevention. Recently, public health messages about the benefits of breastfeeding for both mothers and infants have been heard alongside warnings that breast milk is threatened by the widespread pollution of our environment. Toxic substances such as PCBs, dioxins, pesticides, phthalates, and heavy metals have been found in samples of breast milk from some women in some places. However, no adverse effects on growth or occurrences of illnesses in the first year of life have been attributed to the presence of these chemicals in human milk (*Chemical Compounds in*

Human Milk, by A. Jensen and S. Slorach, Boca Raton: CRC Press, 1991).

What is Safe?

Artificial breast milk substitutes made from cow's milk contain pesticides and chemicals. These products and soy products are also associated with another set of risks, particularly if they are reconstituted with tap water. Bacteria, radioactivity, chemicals and foreign bodies have contaminated milk-based infant formula. Phyto-estrogens and the high aluminum content of soy-based infant formula are also causes of concern. In addition, today, as most commercial soy products are genetically modified, organic soy is necessary for food safety.

The WABA Workshop

Participants included members of La Leche League, WABA, breast-feeding educators, environmentalists, nursing mothers, health promoters, environmental health educators, and others. All agreed that mother's milk is a symbol that is pure, reliable, sustaining, and dependable—a gift of inestimable value. All understood that infant feeding is unique because for many months of rapid development, infants rely on one food—milk—while adults have a more varied diet. They wanted to promote awareness of these issues in the public domain to a much greater extent than at present. They agreed that women have a right to know that the breast milk they produce is as pure as it can be.

Objectives

1. To develop action strategies and language for talking about what passes through mother's bodies into infants' bodies through breast milk; and

2. To discuss a communication strategy that would provide information about relative risks without undermining the objectives of different groups, particularly women's health advocacy groups, breast-feeding, and environmental groups.

A section of the video *"Stopping Carcinogens: Acting in the Face of Scientific Uncertainty"* (featuring biologist Sandra Steingraber) was used. In it, she specifically addresses breast-feeding, environmental toxins, and how they enter the milk. As both a nursing Mother and a scientist/activist, she does this compellingly. Also used was the section of *"Exposure: Environmental Links to Breast Cancer,"* in which Dr. Ana Soto talks about the discovery of nonyl phenol (a hormone disruptor) in plastic tubing used in laboratory experiments on breast cancer and asks "What if baby bottles contain nonyl phenol?" These issues point to the need to (prohibit) avoid hormone disruptors, call for the end to toxic contaminants, and promote the use of safe alternatives—in the case of plastic, a switch to glass bottles (which usually must be ordered) instead of plastic.

Questions

Questions used to stimulate discussion included:

• How do the risks of using "contaminated" breast-milk compare to the risks of not breast-feeding or the risks of contaminated breast milk substitutes?

•What is known about the health consequences for infants who consume "contaminated" food (breast milk, infant formula)?

•How are women responding to conflicting messages about purity/impurity of their breast milk?

•Fetuses appear to be more sensitive to toxic effects than breastfed babies. What are the policy implications of this?

•What do you consider credible arguments on this subject?

•How can we walk the line between media "scare tactics" on the one hand and "suppressing the evidence" on the other?

•What are the political implications of using the term "lifestyle choice" in talking about breast-feeding?

•How can we create a framework to show the relationship between "polluted" breastmilk and other issues related to women's health? (i.e., breast cancer, breast implants, DES, GE foods, HIV/AIDS, poverty, industrial pollution).

Barriers and Problems

Discussion of barriers and problems included the complexity of the issues which influence what is not being said and done. For example, the Centre for Disease Control (CDC) is not looking at dioxins in breast milk because they feel that it would unnecessarily scare people because we don't know what the dangerous level is. They call for a "non-emotional" risk/benefit calculation to determine what to do. Some journalists seek sensational headlines while others refrain from saying things that they know could be inflammatory or could alienate some readership or interests.

Another example is that the World Wildlife Fund (UK) does not say that breast milk is the most toxic substance being eaten, which they feel they could say. Still, others have argued that using human milk as an example to fight pollution will always backfire because it worries mothers and the issues is too complicated for easy comprehension as there are too many unknowns.

Questions for the Guide

Questions for the guide included:

•Have you, or members of your organization, been asked questions about the content of breast milk?

•What "authoritative statements" do you trust and use with confidence (World Health Organization (WHO)? UNICEF? La Leche League International (LLI))?

•What information is available to health professionals on this topic?

•What information do you think should be available? (Your suggestions for phrases, phrases to avoid, etc.)

•Is there any information on contamination that should not go on public information sheets?

•What personal actions can women take to reduce risks to themselves and their infants?

•What political actions must be taken to reduce risks?

•What are some other suggestions, references, or words of wisdom that might make a useful guide on these issues?

•What information is available to mothers?

Actions

Personal:

- Eat lower on the food chain
- Eat organic fruits and vegetables
- Limit consumption of fatty meats and dairy products
- Wash and peel fruits and vegetables (if organic food is not available or affordable)
- Remove skin from chicken
- Avoid crash dieting while breast-feeding
- Choose small fish such as sardines rather than large fish
- Avoid eating Great Lakes fish
- Reduce the use of toxic household cleaners
- Avoid contact with pesticides at work and at home
- Avoid cigarette/cigar smoke (it contains many carcinogens)

Political:

- Link breast-feeding, environmental, and cancer prevention groups
- Find out the location of land use developments in your community
- Explore the possibility that standards for tolerable levels of pollutants should be lower for girls and women
- Lobby Health Canada to replace the "substantial equivalents" principle with environmental risk assessment and food safety assessment
- Set workplace safety standards suitable for pregnant and lactating women
- Make access to cancer incidence in Canada freely available
- Lobby for international conventions such as the WHO/UNICEF Code for the Marketing of Breastmilk Substitutes, and environmental conventions to reduce persistent organic pollutants (POPs)
- "Fax the feds" and tell them to make cleaning up the environment a priority.

By making the reduction of environmental pollution a priority, conditions can be improved. For example, it was noted that levels of toxins found in breast milk fell by around 35% in Europe between 1988 and 1994. Germany's campaign to inform mothers about pollution in the environment influencing breast milk was phrased around "Mother's Milk: A Human Right."

Conclusions

The WABA workshop participants concluded that breast-feeding advocates belong at the forefront of efforts to clean up the environment and need to work with others to do so at all levels. We all need to ask what our governments are doing to protect our children and insist on immediate policy actions to eliminate the production and discharge of toxins.

Common Outcomes

The common outcomes for all three programs included:

Benefits to Community

The outcome of the research acted as a needs assessment, clarifying where the particular groups were in relation to environmental health issues. The guide sheets produced will help serve the needs of each of those communities. However, it should be noted that they were developed from recommendations of particular workshops, thus by their very nature, are incomplete. Different groups have different or culturally specific "takes" on the issues and relationships. Users are urged to adapt them in ways that are suitable for their organizations, communities, health centres, places of learning, other institutional, professional, or policy contexts as appropriate.

The Process as Educational

A collaborative process where all learned and worked together in the development of practical, personal, community and policy related ideas for action.

Addressing Specific Environmental Health Problems

The process provided opportunities to address specific issues within organizations and communities for their cultural/needs contexts.

This project was funded by the National Network on Environments and Women's Health (NNEWH). NNEWH is financially supported by the Centres of Excellence for Women's Health Program, Women's Health Bureau Canada. The views expressed herein do not necessarily represent the views of NNEWH, the Canadian Breast Cancer Foundation or the official policy of Health Canada.

Permission for the reprinting of this paper was received by Dorothy Goldin Rosenberg of the Women's Health and Environments Network as this was first published in "Connections Extra: Women's Health and Environments Network" Issue 15 – extra, Spring/Summer 2000.

Partners and Organizations

Multi Racial Network for Environmental Justice: 61 Sussex Ave., Toronto, ON M5S 1J8; Tel (416) 820 3945; Fax (416) 924 9722

Environmental Centre for New Canadians: 590 Jarvis Street, Toronto, ON M4Y 2J4; Tel (416) 927 1333; Fax (416) 392 0089; E-mail: newcan@ican.net

Greenpeace Canada: 250 Dundas Street West, Toronto, ON M5T 2Z5; Tel (416) 597 8408; Fax (416) 597 8422

Sierra Club of Canada, Eastern Ontario Chapter: 517 College St. #237, Toronto, ON M6G 4A2; Tel (416) 960 9202; Fax (416) 960 0020; E-mail: eastern-canada.chapter@sierraclub.org; www.sierraclub.ca/eastern/

Toronto Environmental Alliance: 30 Duncan St., #201, Toronto, ON M5V 2C3; Tel (416) 596 0660;

Fax (416) 596 1371; E-mail: tea@web.net; www.torontoenvironmental.org

Women's Health and Environments Network (Formerly WNH&E): 517 College St., #233, Toronto, ON M6G 4A2; Tel (416) 928 0880; Fax (416) 928 9640; E-mail: when@web.net; www.web.net/~when

Parents Environmental Network: 51 Tranby Ave., Toronto, ON M5R 1N4; Tel/Fax (416) 960 5495; E-mail: eshough@yorku.ca

Breast Cancer Prevention Coalition (BCPC): 23 Lynden Hill Cres., Brantford, ON N3P 1R1; E-mail: lorna.wilson@sympatico.ca; www.stopcancer.org

Women's Health in Women's Hands: 2 Carleton St., #500, Toronto, ON M5B 1J8; Tel (416) 593 7655; Fax (416) 593 5867

World Alliance for Breast Feeding Action (WABA): Canadian Contact: Penny Van Esterik, Dept. of Anthropology, Vari Hall, York University, 4700 Keele Street, Toronto, ON M3J 1P3; Headquarters: P.O. Box 1200, 10850 Penang, Malaysia; Tel 60 4 658 4816; Fax 60 4 657 2655; E-mail: secr@waba.po.my

The Canadian Centre for Women, Education & Development (CCWED): 700 Kennedy Rd., Scarborough, ON M1K 2B5; Tel (416) 261 3466; Fax (416) 261 3744; E-mail: ccwed@interlog.com

Print Resources

Confronting Environmental Racism: Voices from the Grassroots. Robert D. Bullard, Boston: South End Press, 1993.

Feminist Fables, Suniti Joshi, London: Sheba Feminist Publications, 1990.
Human Rights and Environmental Justice, Sometimes called Military and Environmental Racism in Taking Action for a Healthy Future, Toronto: WNH&E, 1997, Guidebook for the video Exposure

Racism, Sexism, Power and Ideology, Colette Guillaumin, Routledge 1995.

Staying Alive: Women, Ecology and Development, Vandana Shiva, Halifax: Zed, 1989.

Scratching the Surface, Enakasi Dua and Angela Robertson, Toronto: Women's Press, 1999.

Understanding Emissions of Greenhouse Gases in Toronto City, Yuga Onziga, Nov.15, 1998.

Our Stolen Future: Are We Threatening Our Fertility, Intelligence and Survival? A Scientific Detective Story, Colborn, T. et al. Toronto: Dutton Press, 1996.

Rethinking Breast Cancer Risk and the Environment: The Case for the Precautionary Principle, Davis, Devra Lee, Deborah Axelrod, Lisa Bailey, Mitchell Gaynor and Annie Sasco. Environmental Health Perspectivites, Vol 106, No.9, September 1998.

Living Downstream: An Ecologist Looks at Cancer and the Environment, Sandra Steingraber, New York: Addison-Wesley, 1997.

Films/Videos

Films with environmental health/justice context include:

No Grapes: The health impacts of pesticides on Chicana/o farm workers. 18 mins.

Stopping Cancer Where it Starts: The Toxics Links Coalition, environmental justice challenging corporate polluters. 20 mins.

Toxic Partners: Marginalized people in Sydney, NS and Gerogia, US, share their common toxic community experiences and organize for their rights. 30 mins.

Uranium, NFB: Impacts of the nuclear fuel process on Aboriginal people and the earth. 40 mins.

EXPOSURE: Environmental Links to Breast Cancer.

Who's Counting?: Marilyn Waring on Sex, Lies and Global Economics. NFB 70 mins.

Stopping Carcinogens: Acting in the Face of Scientific Uncertainty: Biologist Sandra Steingraber explains toxins in mothers' milk. 35 mins (Available from the Breast Cancer Prevention Coalition).

Section II:
Bibliographic Resources

Representation of Women's Health in General Medical Versus Women's Health Specialty Journals

A Content Analysis

JOCALYN P. CLARK, DEPARTMENT OF PUBLIC HEALTH SCIENCES, UNIVERSITY OF TORONTO AND THE CENTRE FOR RESEARCH IN WOMEN'S HEALTH

GEORGINA D. FELDBERG, DIVISION OF SOCIAL SCIENCE, YORK UNIVERSITY

PAULA A. ROCHON, BAYCREST CENTRE FOR GERIATRIC CARE AND DEPARTMENTS OF MEDICINE AND PUBLIC HEALTH SCIENCES, UNIVERSITY OF TORONTO

Women represent over half the population and use more than 50 percent of health care resources [1,2]. Peer-reviewed journals are health care practitioners' major sources of information about women's health. The leading general medical journals are particularly important because they are prestigious, widely read across clinical, research, and policy disciplines, and elicit news coverage [3,4]. Thus, their content is instrumental in defining "health." Leading causes of women's death and disability include heart disease, lung and breast cancers, depression, and abuse [1,5]. Women's health advocates argue that reproductive and maternal conditions have been over-emphasised in clinical research at the expense of the broad range of health issues contributing to women's disease burden [5]. Indeed, non-traditional women's health concerns have significant impacts on population health and health care costs. Optimal health care for all is said to draw upon a broad definition of women's health that takes into account social, economic, and political contexts [6-8]. This is accomplished by both quantitative and qualitative research methods [9]. Information published in the general medical literature defines the parameters of women's health and fosters its relative importance as a topic of clinical and scholarly concern. Women's health journals, similarly to clinical specialty journals, devote focused attention to a particular area, but have less impact on conventional criteria (Table 1). Women's health journals provide a reflection of the state of the field and their portrayal of women's health may be instructive to general medical journals.

This study compared the representation of women's health in general medical journals with its portrayal in women's health specialty journals.

Methods

Sample selection

Original investigations published in the leading general medical (GM) journals *Annals of Internal Medicine, BMJ, JAMA, Lancet,* and *New England Journal of Medicine (NEJM)* published between January 1 and June 30, 1999 were compared to original investigations published in leading women's health specialty (WS) journals *Health Care for Women International, Journal of Women's Health & Gender-based Medicine (JWH), Women & Health,* and *Women's Health Issues* for the same time period (Table 2). Only original investigations studying adult human populations were included, providing an initial sample of 514 GM and 82 WS articles.

Identification of women's health articles

All WS articles were included and three strategies were used to identify GM articles with a women's

Table 1

Quality indicators of leading general medical and women's health specialty journals

Journal (Location)	Impact Factor [*]	Citation rate Immediacy Index [*]	Current Circulation [†]	Inclusion in MEDLINE
General medical				
Annals (U.S)	10.097	1.959	91,097	Yes
BMJ (U.K.)	5.143	1.992	117,000	Yes
JAMA (U.S.)	11.435	3.728	3,705,000	Yes
Lancet (U.K.)	10.197	2.634	45,000	Yes
NEJM (U.S.)	28.857	6.445	183,000	Yes
Women's health speciality				
HCWI (U.K.)	NR	NR	612	Yes
JWH (U.S.)	1.038	0.128	5,000	Yes
W&H (U.S.)	0.974	0.186	1,225	Yes
WHI (U.S.)	0.404	0.031	3,000	Yes

[*] Institute for Scientific Information or Social Science Citation Index Journal Citation Reports, 1999. Impact factor is a measure of the frequency with which the "average article" in a journal has been cited in a particular year, calculated by dividing the number of current citations to articles published in the two pervious years by the total number of articles published in the two previous years. Immediacy Index is a measure of how quickly the "average article" in a journal is cited, calculated by dividing the number of citations to articles published in a given year by the number of articles published in that year. Higher values indicate higher impact. [†] Current circulation obtained from Ulrich's International Periodicals Directory, 39th Edition, 2001 and/or confirmed by communication with publisher. NR = not ranked Annals = Annals of Internal Medicine, BMJ = British Medical Journal, JAMA = Journal of the American Medical Association, NEJM = New England Journal of Medicine HCWI = Health Care for Women International, JWH = Journal of Women's Health & Gender-based Medicine, W&H = Women & Health, WHI = Women's Health Issues

health focus. First, we (JPC, PAR) identified all 88 articles that studied women-only samples. Second, three independent reviewers (JPC, PAR, PdN) read all 514 titles and conducted searches for keywords: "woman," "women," "female," "sex," or "gender," those related to female-specific conditions (e.g., breast cancer, fertility, estrogen, etc.), and keywords related to social determinants of health generally (e.g., education, social, equity, poverty, etc.). Results of the keyword searches were compared and consensus reached. Eighty-nine articles were identified, 11 of which were supplementary to the first method of identification. Third, a MEDLINE search was conducted for the following medical subject headings: "women's health," "women's health services," and "women." Limiting the MEDLINE search to the journals in our sample and the time period of study, 16 articles resulted, only 4 of which were original investigations; none of these were supplementary. Using these three search strategies, 99 GM articles with a women's health focus were identified. A more detailed review (JPC) confirmed all GM and WS articles contained women's health content and met the original inclusion criteria.

Content analysis of articles

We developed a semi-structured content analysis instrument to assess sample characteristics, study design, and health topic evaluated in each article. Study design was identified and classified according to a standard taxonomy [10,11] modified to include qualitative research (i.e., randomised controlled trial (RCT), cohort, case-control, cross-sectional, case report, or qualitative) and health topic was identified and examined using an approach consistent with other investigators [12-14]. All health topics were then classified according to definition of women's health used [9]: Traditional, non-traditional, or both. Traditional topics involved reproductive conditions. i.e., fertility, pregnancy, childbirth, breastfeeding, menstruation, menopause, hormone replacement therapy, and female-specific cancers such as breast, cervical, endometrial, and ovarian. Non-traditional topics were all other health conditions, including those which afflict women to a greater extent than men such as abuse, osteoporosis, and eating disorders. Articles classified as drawing on "both" definitions evaluated, as an example, depression in pregnancy.

The instrument was pilot tested on 10 articles. Two independent coders (JPC, GDF) reviewed articles. Interrater reliability ranged from 91% to 100% agreement per item. Coders had 91% agreement on health topic classification. Discrepancies were resolved by consensus.

Results

Among the 514 GM articles in our sample, 99 (19.2%) were related to women's health. Most of these 99 appeared in *Lancet* (26.3%), *BMJ* (23.2%), and *NEJM* (22.2%). Eighty-eight (88.9%) of the GM women's health articles reported on women-only study samples; the remaining 11 (11.1%) were of mixed-gender. Most of the 82 WS articles appeared in *JWH* (37.8%) and *Women & Health* (29.3%). Similarly to the GM articles, 87.8% of the WS articles reported on women-only study samples.

Representation of women's health issues (Table 3)

To compare how women's health issues were represented, we categorised articles into three mutually exclusive groups: Traditional, non-traditional, or both. The distribution of topics was significantly different between GM and WS journals ($X2 = 13$; $p = 0.0013$). Fifty-three (53.5%) of the 99 GM articles addressed solely a traditional women's health topic. Of these, 26 (49.1%) related to reproductive health issues and 27 (50.9%) studied female-specific cancers. In contrast, 22 (26.8%) WS articles focused solely on traditional women's health. Of these, 15 (68.2%) related to reproduction and 7 (31.8%) to female cancers.

Twenty-seven (27.3%) of the GM articles concerned a women's health topic more broadly defined and were categorised as non-traditional women's health: heart disease (n = 6), health care delivery (n = 3), HIV/AIDS/STDs (n = 3), musculoskeletal conditions such as osteoporosis (n = 3), obesity/physical activity (n = 3), and a range of other women's health topics (n = 9). With respect to WS articles, 34 (41.5%) addressed solely a non-traditional women's health topic: obesity/physical activity (n = 7), general health (n = 5), musculoskeletal (n = 4), depression (n = 3), heart disease (n = 3), HIV/AIDS/STDs (n = 3), and a range of topics (n = 9).

Nineteen (19.2%) of the GM women's health articles addressed *both* a traditional and non-

Table 2

Sections containing original investigations in leading general medical and women's health specialty journals

Journal	Section
General medical	
Annals	Articles
	Academia and Clinic
BMJ	Papers
	General Practice
JAMA	Original Contributions
	Caring for the Critically Ill
	Preliminary Communication
	Clinical Investigations
Lancet	Articles
	Early Reports
NEJM	Articles
	Special Articles
Women's health specialty	
HCWI	Articles
JWH	Original Articles
W&H	Articles
WHI	Articles

traditional women's health topic, compared to 26 (31.7%) WS articles which incorporated both types of women's health. While overall more than 40% of both GM and WS articles related in some way to women's reproduction, WS articles much more frequently combined this narrow women's health topic with a non-traditional issue (e.g. HIV in pregnancy). Specifically, 42 GM articles focused on reproduction, of which 16 (42.4%) incorporated a non-traditional issue, while 24 of 39 (61.5%) WS articles combined both perspectives. This combined approach reflects the broad, contextual definition of women's health advocated by scholars, practitioners, and patients [8,9].

Only one (1.0%) article published in GM journals used a non-quantitative research method. The others reported on RCT (n = 30), cohort (n = 38), case-control (n = 11), cross-sectional (n = 14), and case report (n = 5) designs. In contrast, a full 40% of WS articles involved qualitative or mixed

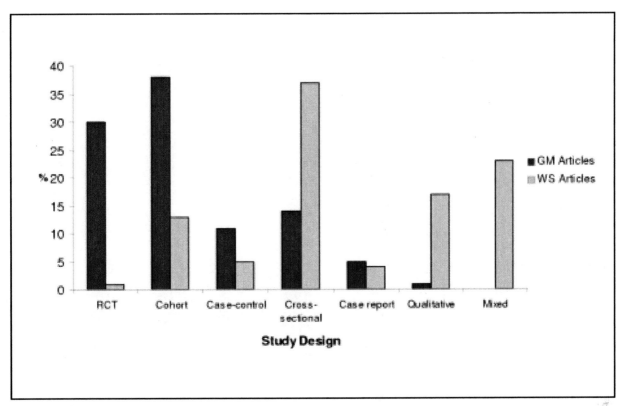

Figure 1: This figure compares the proportions of women's health articles published in general medical (GM) versus women's health specialty (WS) journals according to the study design used.

methodologies, as advocated by women's health scholars [5,15]. The remaining WS studies were dominated by the cross-sectional (n = 30) design (Figure 1).

Discussion

Our study offers valuable insight into the presence and nature of women's health content in general medical versus women's health journals. Among the GM journals, each devoted approximately 20% of their original investigations content to women's health. This is encouraging and may reflect burgeoning scholarship of women's health researchers, government initiatives, and leadership of medical editors to include comprehensive approaches to health care. However, most GM articles drew on a narrow definition of women's health. WS journals provided more balanced coverage of women's health, publishing articles that addressed key women's health topics in context, more broadly defined, and based on mixed quantitative-qualitative methodologies. These integrated approaches are in keeping with principles designed to promote women's health across all clinical and research disciplines.

Leading sources of women's death and disability were not well represented across either set of journals. Lung cancer is the leading cancer killer of women but was not the focus of any articles published during the first half of 1999; in contrast, breast and cervical cancer articles together accounted for one-fifth of the entire sample. No GM articles and only five (6.1%) WS articles addressed violence against women. Likewise, heart disease produces significant illness burdens for women, but accounted for only 6% of articles in our entire sample.

The representation of women's health in WS journals is an important yardstick for the general

Table 3

Comparison between women's health original investigations in leading general medical versus women's health specialty journals

GENERAL MEDICAL JOURNALS		WOMEN'S HEALTH SPECIALTY JOURNALS	
Characteristic	N	Characteristic	N
Journal		**Journal**	
Annals	10 (10.1%)	*HCWI*	20 (24.4%)
BMJ	23 (23.2%)	*JWH*	31 (37.8%)
JAMA	18 (18.2%)	*W&H*	24 (29.3%)
Lancet	26 (26.3%)	*WHI*	7 (8.5%)
NEJM	22 (22.2%)		
Total	99	**Total**	82
Representation of Women's Health		**Representation of Women's Health**	
Traditional	53 (53.5%)	Traditional	22 (26.8%)
Reproduction	26	Reproduction	15
Female cancer	27	Female cancer	7
Non-traditional	27 (27.3%)	Non-traditional	34 (41.5%)
Heart disease	6	Obesity/physical activity	7
Health care	3	General health	5
HIV/AIDS/STDs	3	Musculoskeletal	4
Musculoskeletal	3	Depression/mental health	3
Obesity/physical activity	3	Heart disease	3
Other	9	HIV/AIDS/STDs	3
		Other	9
Incorporating Both Traditional and Non-traditional	19 (19.2%)	Incorporating Both Traditional and Non-traditional	26 (31.7%)
Reproduction & other	16	Reproduction & other	24
Female cancer & other	3	Female cancer & other	2
Total	99	**Total**	82

medical literature which has greater influence on the health message communicated to practitioners and the public. Recently, *JAMA* published a second special theme issue on women's health (the only leading GM journal thus far) that included a range of topics such as heart disease, ovarian cancer, and HIV [16]. This is a significant leadership move because theme issues draw attention to health topics and imply topic importance; indeed, readers appear to prioritise women's health [17,18]. In addition, *Lancet* recently published a six-part series on violence against women that will surely raise the profile of violence's impact on women's health. Where possible, a better strategy might be to profile the range of women's health topics regularly, rather than under the auspices of special issues and series.

On conventional criteria, GM journals clearly have more impact (i.e., circulation, citation rate) than WS journals, appear to publish articles higher up the hierarchy of evidence (i.e., RCTs and intervention studies), and thus likely publish articles of superior quality. This may mean that health topics less amenable to RCT design (e.g., abuse) stand a better chance of publication in non-GM journals. Regardless, the focus of GM journals on "navel-to-knees" women's health may contribute to an uneven evidence base regarding women's health care. GM journals are challenged to maintain scientific excellence while incorporating the range of topics reflective of women's lives and health care needs. Precisely because GM journals have wide impact, it would be of benefit for editorial decisions and peer review mechanisms to promote a broader conceptualisation of women's health.

Limitations

We chose a particular time period, but our study provides an important preliminary audit of a developing field. Second, our results may not be generalisable to all medical and women's health journals, but it is unlikely that less prestigious journals provide better women's health coverage. We only evaluated original investigations and it is possible that issues relevant to broadening the definition of women's health are discussed in reviews and editorials. However, original investigations are important for leading new scientific understanding. Finally, we relied upon a primarily quantitative method. Additional in-depth and qualitative analysis of the medical literature, including its quality across types of journals, would enhance explorations of the representation of women's health.

Conclusions

Most women's health articles in the general medical literature represented traditional conditions, while specialty journal articles were more likely to address non-traditional topics. Neither type of journal well represented leading sources of women's death and disability. Since women's reproductive and maternal capacities represent only a fraction of women's health issues, leading journals should include articles about women's health that incorporate social, economic and political contexts. Because the leading general medical journals have wide impact, it would be of benefit for editorial decisions and peer review to promote a broader conceptualisation of women's health.

Competing Interests

None declared.

Authors' contributions

JPC conceived of the study, collected data, and drafted the manuscript. GDF and PAR contributed to study design and acquisition of data. All authors obtained funding, contributed to analysis and interpretation of data, and read and approved the final manuscript.

Acknowledgements

JPC is a doctoral fellow of the Canadian Institutes for Health Research (CIHR) and the Inner City Health Research Unit, University of Toronto, and is the 2001 Mitchell/Venn Fellow in Women's Health. PAR is supported by an Investigator Award from CIHR. The work was also facilitated by the National Network on Environments and Women's Health with funding from the Centres of Excellence Programme, Health Canada. Financial support from these sources is gratefully acknowledged. We also wish to thank M. Binns, P. de Nobrega, J. Dergal, D. Laxer, and A. Misra for their assistance.

A version of this paper was presented at the Fourth International Congress on Peer Review in Biomedical Publication, Barcelona Spain, September 16, 2001.

References

1. Misra, D., editor: *Women's Health Data Book: A Profile of Women's Health in the United States.* [http://www.jiwh.org/databook.htm]The Henry J. Kaiser Family Foundation and the Jacobs Institute of Women's Health, 2002.

2. Moore, R., Yang, M., Zhang, J., Clarke, K.: *Economic Burden of Illness in Canada.* [http://www.hc-sc.gc.ca/hpb/lcdc/publicat/burden/burd4_e.html] Ottawa: Health Canada, 1997.

3. Fletcher, R.H., Fletcher, S.W.: The future of medical journals in the western world. *Lancet* 1998, 352: SII30-3.

4. Smith, R.: What is publication? A continuum. *BMJ* 1999, 318: 142.

5. National Forum on Health: *Final Report: An Overview of Women's Health.* [http://wwwnfh.hc-sc.gc.ca/publicat/finvol2/women/idxwomen.htm] Ottawa: Health Canada, 1997.

6. Phillips, S.: The social context of women's health: goals and objectives for medical education. *Can Med Assoc J* 1995, 152: 507-511.

7. Office on Women's Health: The National Women's Health Information Center. [http://www.4women.gov] U.S. Department of Health and Human Services, 2000.

8. Cohen, M., Sinding, C.: Changing concepts of women's health: Advocating for change. [http://www.hc-sc.gc.ca/canusa/papers/advocate.htm] In: *Canada-USA Forum on Women's Health Ottawa*, Health Canada, 1996.

9. Greaves, L.: *CIHR 2000: Sex, Gender and Women's Health.* [http://www.bccewh.bc.ca/pdf.htm#cihr] Vancouver British Columbia Centre of Excellence for Women's Health, 1999.

10. Hadorn, D.C., Baker, D., Hodges, J.S., Hicks, N.: Rating the quality of evidence for clinical practice guidelines. *J Clin Epidemid* 1996, 49: 749-754.

11. Guyatt, G.H., Sackett, D.L., Sinclair, J.C., Hayward, R., Cook, D.J., Cook, R.J.: Users' guides to the medical literature IX : A method for grading health care recommendations. *JAMA* 1995, 274: 1800-1804.

12. Lewison, G., Grant, J., Jansen, P. P.: International gastroenterology research: Subject areas, impact, and funding. *Gut* 2001, 49: 295-302.

13. Moncrieff, J., Crawford, M.J.: British psychiatry in the 20th century: Observations from a psychiatric journal. *Soc Sci Med* 2001, 53:349-356.

14. Woolf, S.H., Johnson, R.E.: A one-year audit of topics and domains in the Journal of the American Medical Association and the New England Journal of Medicine. *Am J Prev Med* 2000, 19: 79-86.

15. National Institutes of Health (NIH), Office of the Director: *Agenda for Research on Women's Health for the 21st Century.* Washington, DC: U.S. Department of Health and Human Services, 1999.

16. DeAngelis, C.D., Winker, M.A.: Women's health—filling the gaps. *JAMA* 2001, 285: 1508-1509.

17. Delamothe, T.: Forthcoming theme issues and how we chose them. *BMJ* 2001, 323: 766.

18. Lundberg, G.D., Paul, M.C., Fritz, H.: A comparison of the opinions of experts and readers as to what topics a general medical journal should address. *JAMA* 1998, 280: 288-290.

The Restructuring of Work and Women's Health
An Annotated Bibliography

JOAN M. EAKIN, DEPARTMENT OF PUBLIC HEALTH SCIENCES, UNIVERSITY OF TORONTO
ANN SYLVIA BROOKER, INSTITUTE FOR WORK AND HEALTH
WITH PAT ARMSTRONG, CECELIA BENOIT, IRENE JANSEN, BARBARA NEIS,
LYNN SKILLEN AND WOMEN, WORK AND HEALTH GROUP

Profound alterations in the economy, the labour force and the organization and nature of work in the last decades of the twentieth century have had enormous consequences for society and for workers in general. The research of the Women, Work and Health Group of NNEWH focuses on the implications of such restructuring for the health of women. This Annotated Bibliography was conceived as a contribution to this research endeavour. Its purpose is to assemble what is currently known about this issue and to assist in the conceptualization of the notion of "restructuring" and its relationship to women's health. It is intended to be a resource to researchers in the formulation of particular research projects, and to others interested in policy and change in this area.

The primary objective of developing the bibliography is to uncover what is known specifically about the health effects for women of work restructuring. There are voluminous literatures on the various components of this topic (i.e. on the nature of economic and labour force changes, women's health, women and work, women and unpaid work) but literature linking these components is scarce, as is literature that explicitly investigates the health implications of these issues. The bibliography focuses on literature of most direct relevance to the topic, but does include some literature in areas of indirect or partial relevance (see section outlining the rationale and focus of the bibliography). In these areas, however, the bibliography includes only an illustrative sample of key concepts and knowledge and makes no claims whatsoever to being comprehensive. The bibliography strives only to be a first step in identifying relevant bodies of literature and in initiating their integration and synthesis.

This document first outlines the search strategy and clarifies choices made regarding inclusion and exclusion of various literatures and topics. This is followed by the annotated bibliography proceeded by an explanation of the conceptual organization of the bibliography and the format used to summarize individual references.

Literature Search Process

Data Bases

The following databases were searched:
C MedLine 1976-1997
C Healthstar 1975-1997
C CINAHL 1982-1997
C Social Science Abstracts 1983-1997
C Sociofile 1974-1997
C NIOSH

Search Strategy

References were obtained from electronic and manual searches. The manual search used the citations of key articles, the personal bibliographic records of NNEWH Women, Work and Health Group members, the reference list of McMaster University/University of Toronto's Quality of Nursing WorkLife Research Unit, references from the working paper list of York University's Centre for Health Studies, and the internal library of the Institute for Work and Health.

The electronic searches were conducted using key word strategies in three topic areas: restructuring, work organization and new forms of work. In the social science databases, health (or its synonyms) was added as a further criterion. The searches were conducted as follows:

1) *Restructuring*
restructuring, downsizing, re-designing, sub-contracting, re-engineering, rightsizing, globalization **or** out-sourcing
AND
work, labour, employment, occupation, or job

2) *New forms of work*
contingent, contract, tele-work, part-time and emotional work
AND
work, labour, employment, occupation, or job
AND
women or woman

3) *Work organization*
work organization, lean production.

This search was used to generate a list of the terms used to describe current trends in work organization (e.g. flexible specialisation, post-Fordism, lean production). The terms identified were then themselves searched.

Focus

From the references generated by these searches, decisions were made about which ones to acquire for review and which ones to include in the Bibliography. The focus of the Bibliography is on the following:

Literature relevant to contemporary restructuring trends. We searched the literature as far back as the mid 1970s and included "old" references if they appeared to have relevance to restructuring issues as they are understood in the 1990s.

Restructuring trends that are general rather than specific. The Bibliography focuses primarily on trends that affect society as a whole. Thus, literature on the reorganization of particular workplaces was not included where it appeared idiosyncratic or non-representative of more general issues.

Restructuring trends of most relevance to Canada. Articles pertaining to industrialised countries (especially Great Britain and the USA) were examined more carefully than were those pertaining to developing countries. This focus is not intended to suggest that restructuring does not have important implications for developing nations, or that we have nothing to learn from their experience. Particularly, this focus should not obscure the possibility that the restructuring of western capitalism involves the exploitation of women in developing countries.

The restructuring of work. Restructuring is occurring at many levels and in many segments of society, including global economic systems, particular economic formations such as capitalism, the labour force, and the restructuring of work and the workplace. This annotated bibliography focused in particular on the restructuring of work and the workplace. However, because the restructuring of work occurs within the context of the restructuring at a more macro level (e.g. of the state, or of capitalism), some articles on these topics are included.

Health implications. There is a vast body of literature of obvious relevance to the topic of restructuring, women and health but which does not address the health aspect. For example, the literature on general economic restructuring (noted in the previous point), and the literature on women and unpaid work, or women and the welfare state is clearly of general relevance to our topic. This literature is extensive and diverse, but it is not included in this collection unless it makes explicit reference to matters of health. Likewise, although there is considerable literature on the impact of restructuring on women's health, only literature that sees the impact as being through work is included in the bibliography (e.g. the consequences of health care restructuring for women's access to medical care would not be included here).

Health care restructuring and health care workers. There is a large and growing body of literature on the restructuring of medical care. Items from this literature were only included if they discussed the impact of health care restructuring on those who work in this employment sector, particularly women workers.

Health effects of downsizing but not job loss. There is a growing literature on the consequences of downsizing. At least three categories of literature can be distinguished: 1) the health effects of the threat of redundancy (including the literature specifically on job insecurity), 2) the health effects of downsizing on those who are not laid off (the "survivors"), and 3) the health effects of downsizing and job loss on those who actually lose their jobs (including the health consequences of unemployment). This third category of literature is *not* included in this bibliography. The literature on job insecurity is substantial, and includes predominantly psychologically oriented literature on the productivity and human wellbeing implications of job insecurity as an aspect of work experience. Only some of this literature is included in this bibliography, generally that which addresses the issue in relation specifically to organizational change/restructuring.

Format

Entries in the Annotated Bibliography are alphabetical by first author. Each citation is annotated in the following way:

Perspective: This entry attempts to characterize the general point of view or orientation of the item, referring to either/and discipline (e.g. sociology, industrial relations), theoretical framework (e.g. political economy, feminism), or interest group (e.g. management, professional service).

Setting: This entry indicates the primary location or context of the data, study or discussion, especially country or region.

References: This entry includes the number of references cited in the item, to give a sense of its potential scholarly scope and promise as a source of further references.

Type: This entry characterizes the primary methodology or approach used in the item, for example if it is a review article, a discussion piece, or an empirical survey.

Summary: This entry offers a précis of the article's content, with emphasis on what is most relevant to women, work and health. More detail is provided on items that are closer to the main topic of the bibliography. Where it is not clear from the text, observations or comments that come from the reviewers as opposed to the authors are put in [square brackets]. No explicit critique of the articles' methods or theoretical framework is provided in these summaries. However, in many cases the descriptions of how the authors conducted their studies and reached conclusions offer readers the opportunity to generate their own (preliminary) critiques - acknowledging, of course, that a thorough critique would require an in-depth reading of the original paper.

Annotated Bibliography

Abraham, K.G. (1990). "Restructuring the employment relationship: the growth of market-mediated work arrangements" in K. Abraham and R. McKersie (Eds.) *New Developments in the Labor Market*, Cambridge, MA: MIT Press.

Perspective: Economic, business
Setting: American
References: 40
Type of article/study: descriptive, plus a survey

Summary: The author presents evidence from surveys to show that there has been a steady growth in market-mediated work relationships in the US since the 1970s. The author estimates that market-mediated work accounts for approximately 10% of total employment in the USA.

The author uses survey data to help determine employers' reasons for using market-mediated employment services. These include: lower labour costs (especially for low skill work), increased volatility of the economic environment (i.e. in terms of volatile demand for the firm's products and services) and the use of specialised services which cannot be conducted in-house at a reasonable cost. This article is a good source for US data on the prevalence of alternative work arrangements. It is also useful as it presents the rationale for employing contingent workers from the perspective of the employer.

Amott, T. (1993). Shortchanged: Restructuring women's work. In T. Amott, *Caught in the Crisis: Women and the U.S. Economy Today*, Chapter 3, Monthly Review Press: New York.

Perspective: economics, labour, feminist
Setting: USA in the last 20 years
References: 41
Type of article/study: descriptive/discussion

Summary: This book discusses trends in the U.S. labour force in the last 20 years. Amott argues that in the last 20 years, to cut costs, companies have hired women in lieu of men, as women are less likely to be unionized and more likely to accept temporary work with no benefits. Between 1979 and 1989, women were slightly less likely to lose their jobs than men were. Other general trends in the economy include: union-busting, capital flight (which primarily affects the manufacturing sector), and the increased use of home workers. Capital flight and corporate downsizing lost millions of workers their jobs. Decreasing unionisation has negative implications for items on labour's agenda including health and safety legislation, child care and health benefits. Home workers are more likely to be living in poverty than other workers, and they often work in dangerous conditions (e.g. semiconductor manufacturing homework). There has been an increasing trend towards restructuring the work force around a core and ring (contingent workers) concept. Firms can hire contingent workers either individually (e.g. by hiring "the self-employed") or by sub-contracting out to smaller (perhaps underground) firms. As the economic crisis worsened, many companies sub-contracted out work in the informal sector (or "underground" economy). These underground firms hire undocumented workers and escape health and safety, minimum wage and environmental regulation. Increased unemployment provides a ready supply of workers for these firms. Women and men of colour are the groups of workers most likely to be found in the informal sector. Although the number of women-owned businesses doubled between 1977 and 1987, 40% of these had receipts of less than $5000 a year. Given the tenuous nature of such employment and the fact that many of these businesses could not provide pensions or benefits, one could essentially classify much of self-employment as contingent work. Reduced earnings means more work for women in the home such as cleaning, cooking, and care giving [which have implications for women's health].

Amott, T. (1993). **From poor to rich, from women to men: Restructuring the state.** In T. Amott, *Caught in the Crisis: Women and the Economy Today.* New York: Monthly Review Press.

Perspective: sociological, feminist
Setting: USA
References: 41
Type of article/study: descriptive/discussion

Summary: This book is set in the context of America in the aftermath of the conservative Reagan and Bush Sr. agenda. The article discusses the deregulation of affirmative action programs and occupational health and safety legislation, and a reduction in staffing and enforcement. The article describes how government tax cuts favoured the wealthy at the expense of the poor and those of moderate income. Further, there were spending cuts to those programs that helped out families with children, and poor families. As women are generally poorer than men, they rely disproportionately on these programs. [Although set in the US, many of these trends appear to be occurring in Canada as well.]

Appelbaum, E. (1987). **Restructuring work: temporary, part time and at-home employment.** In H. Harmann (Ed.), *Computer Chips and Paper Clips* (268-310). Washington D.C: National Academy Press.

Perspective: Economic
Setting: U.S.A.
References: 33 articles and 26 additional references to statistical data sources.
Type of article/study: Descriptive. Many statistical data are presented, as well as informal interview data on the impact of technological change on the work schedules of women.

Summary: The author notes the significant growth in involuntary part-time work and temporary employment. Bureau of Labor statistics are cited to demonstrate the steady increase in the number of people employed in temporary help services (for women: from 255 per 40,000 in 1982 to 400 per 40,000 in 1984—or 1% of the U.S .work force). Women comprise about two-thirds of these workers (p.279). In 1967, about 16% of the civilian employed labour force was part-time, whereas, by 1985, it was about

20%. Two-thirds of these part-time workers are women (p. 286-287). The author notes the steady increase in the number of part-time workers who would rather be working full-time. The author notes that technological improvements (e.g. computers) have facilitated the trend towards increased "home work" or tele-commuting. Nonetheless, it has been the reduction in labor costs (e.g. no benefits; reduced overhead—often these workers must provide their own equipment) which has been the driving force behind the development of alternative work schedules. The savings to companies of shifting health insurance and other costs to employees are substantial.

Appelbaum distinguishes between two types of at-home employment: (1) low-skilled home workers who perform clerical functions (or manufacturing) and who are often paid piece rate, and are rarely paid benefits (such workers are cheaper for the company than on-site workers), and (2) professional workers who *choose* to work from home (usually because it reduces commuting time, or provides flexibility). Workers in this latter group have more control over the scheduling of work than do more highly supervised, unskilled home workers. There are some limited data to suggest that these professional home workers are more likely to be permanent full-time employees receiving full salaries and benefits. Employers use this type of labour in order to keep high-skilled and fairly irreplaceable workers who might otherwise quit.

The disadvantages of working at home are noted: reduced access to communication flows, reduced "informal" collaboration between employees, and little or no spatial and temporal segregation between home and office. Appelbaum notes that for women, decisions about the number of hours they work are severely constrained by the lack of affordable, quality day care (p. 283). A substantial number of women workers (p. 304) "choose" [i.e. make a choice given the societal constraints they face] flexible work schedules in order to meet both home and work responsibilities. But the negative effects of these arrangements on career mobility and/or earnings growth are a concern even for those who choose those options (p. 305). The author notes that companies that experience cyclical demands, or who expect automation to reduce employment needs appear to be staffing at less than full needs even during periods of economic expansion, and are organizing employment needs via the ring and core concept to reduce lay-off in the future (p. 306). [Lay-offs of full-time staff presumably have costs associated with them]. Appelbaum concludes her article by expressing concern that these labour market changes "may signal a restructuring of employment opportunities and the extension of sub-par working conditions to sectors of the economy where full-time work and benefits had usually [previously] prevailed" (p. 306).

This article provides some good American data on the prevalence of alternative forms of work. Furthermore, the author attempts to understand both the business rationale for the observed labour market changes and also examines the impact of these changes on women workers.

Armstrong, P. (1997). Restructuring the private and the public. In S. B. Boyd (Ed.). *Challenging the Public/Private Divide. Feminism, Health and Public Policy.* Toronto: University of Toronto Press.

Perspective: sociological, feminist
Setting: Canada
References: ~ 44
Type of article/study: Discussion, historical description

Summary:This paper provides a historical description of the restructuring of the public and private sectors and their impact on women and on their work from the post-Second World War era to the present. The public sector as provider, regulator and employer are discussed. The most recent changes noted by Armstrong include the following: Public sector spending, which grew from the 1950s to the 1980s, has in recent times come under attack. The attack has primarily come in the name of reducing the debt and of making government more efficient. The private and the public are being dramatically redefined in ways that will have a profound impact on women. In the public sector, the civil service is being downsized dramatically. This can mean greater work intensification for those women who remain employed. These factors are particularly pertinent for women given that so many women work in the public sector. Other women have become unemployed or are re-employed doing work that has been transferred to the private sector. However, this private sector work is less likely to be protected by union contract, and is less likely to be full-time and permanent. In addition, many agencies that were at least nominally established to protect women's interests within the state have been cancelled (e.g. the Canadian Advisory Council on the Status of Women) or dismantled. Governments at all levels are significantly reducing funding for education, health and welfare.

These cutbacks have a significant impact on women as both providers and users, especially given that women constitute the majority of both providers and users. Services (such as at home health care) which are not provided by paid workers are being transferred to women in the home or to voluntary agencies. Armstrong notes: "The restructuring currently underway means both more unpaid work and less protection for women, in terms of social support, unionization or regulation. It also means more responsibility and less power" (p.36).

Armstrong, P., Choiniere, J., Feldberg, G., White, J., and Rosenberg H. *Voices from the Ward: a Pilot Study of the Impact of Cutbacks on Hospital Care. Occasional paper, Toronto: York University Centre for Health Studies.*

Perspective: sociological, patient/system and employee perspective
Setting: nine hospitals within urban and rural settings, that are located in both northern and southern Ontario.
Type of study: descriptive study based on focus group interviews
References: 7

Summary: Although most of the results of this study pertain to the impact of cut backs on patient care, there are some results which pertain to the effect on employees. Only these latter results are covered by this summary. Attempts were made to interview RNAs, NAs, dietary and housekeeping workers in each institution, in a focus group setting, by occupation or in interviews. The same open-ended questions were used in each session. In addition, as a basis of comparison, one mixed group of workers, from the same department, was also included from each institution in order to gather varied perspectives of the same situation in the same department. The authors primarily focussed on responses which re-occurred and which had no substantial refutation in other interviews.

The impact of restructuring on the hospital employees includes: fatigue due to increased workload, increased tension, loss of control, fear of job loss, lower resistance and greater vulnerability to disease (in an environment where infections are common). The fast work pace and performance of repetitive work tasks have the effect of increasing on-the-job injuries. Increased tensions in the workplace are caused by new work schedules and regimens, greater surveillance, loss of control and fear of job loss. Increased tensions lead to a workplace in which people cry, scream at each other, and get upset. Untrained, inexperienced and part time workers are used by the hospital in order to cut costs, but this often places additional burdens on the full-time staff.

Armstrong, P. (1996). The feminisation of the labour force: Harmonizing down in a global economy. In: I. Bakker (Ed.). *Rethinking Restructuring Gender and Change in Canada.* **Toronto: University of Toronto Press.**

Perspective: sociological
Setting: Canada
References: references to Statistics Canada data only.

Summary: The author notes that restructuring for the global economy has meant the disappearance of full-time jobs in all but the non-commercial services and services to businesses. Part time work has been increasing. Even in full-time work, hours and shift work has increased, as has job insecurity. This paper provides a good overview of recent labour force restructuring in Canada. It focuses on the 1990-1992 period and has used data from Statistics Canada.

Armstrong-Stassen, M., Cameron, S.J. and Horsburgh, M.E. (1996). The impact of organizational downsizing on the job satisfaction of nurses. *Canadian Journal of Nursing Administration*, **9 (4): 8-32.**

Perspective: nursing, psychological, nursing administration
Setting: 3 community hospitals in southwestern Ontario
References: 38
Type of article/study: survey

Summary: Surveys were given to 258 registered nurses (RNs) and 87 registered practical nurses (RPNs) at two different time periods: in 1991, when hospitals were still experiencing a shortage of nurses, and in 1992, following a hospital restructuring which involved the closing of beds, the relocation of nurses to other units and the layoff of some nursing staff. Over the course of the study, nurses showed a marked reduction in satisfaction regarding their future careers, identification with their hospital, supervision, and co-workers. However, these nurses did not experience significant change with respect to their satisfaction with the kind of work they performed, the amount of their work, or their physical work conditions. The authors suggest that their working conditions were protected because these nurses belonged to a professional nurses' association and their collective bargaining contract contained provisions about the kind of work, amount of work and working conditions that their employer is required to meet. The nurses reported a significant increase in their satisfaction with their financial rewards. The authors attribute this finding to the collective agreement reached in 1991, which raised the maximum salary of nurses by 29 percent over a two year period and to pay equity legislation which was also able to raise nurses' wages. The authors conclude by suggesting that organizations experiencing downsizing should have effective communication strategies, and should have supervisors that are supportive and helpful to their employees. These recommendations are based on a report which they cite (by Right Associates) as well as previous research done by Armstrong-Stassen in 1994 (which relates to the latter recommendation).

Bains, A. (1998). *Thirty eight cents a shirt.* **Toronto Life, February.**

Perspective: sympathetic to the plight of home textile workers
Setting: Toronto
References: none
Type of article/study: journalistic article

Summary: This journalist does an investigation into textile home workers. She interviews three women who work together as sewers and who, after one week of labour in which they work overtime, have $400 to split between them (amounting to well below the minimum wage).

Minimum wage for home workers is 10% above the regular minimum wage of $7.54/hour, to account for the use of space and utilities in their home. Since the free trade agreement was signed, thousands of jobs in the garment industry have disappeared and large corporations have opened operations in the third world. However, a representative of the union UNITE points out that sub-contracting and home working allows flexibility for retailers, as they do not have to wait for overseas shipments, and can get replacement orders in a matter of days. But given the international competition, there is a continuing pressure to push down wages. In Toronto, estimates of the number of home-workers range from 4,000 to 8,000.

The Advisory Committee for Ladies' Dress and Sportswear has three inspectors who are able to give warnings, fines and court orders for prosecution. However, they have insufficient staff to keep up with the work load. The Ministry of Labour employment practices branch can also prosecute employers. However, their branch operates mostly by receiving complaints. Yet many of the home workers are immigrants and are unaware of their rights, or do not complain for fear of retribution. Further, inspectors (from either the advisory committee or from the Ministry) cannot enter into private homes.

To aggravate the situation, the current Ontario government passed a regulatory amendment that decreases the time to file a complaint against an employer from two years to six months, and limits maximum claims to $10,000. In the U.S., the federal Department of Labour posts lists of companies that violate labour standards. In Canada, however, provision of information of this sort does not exist. Furthermore, Canada has privacy laws which would prevent our government from doing the same. Health effects reported by the home workers include: eye strain, backaches, leg and hand cramps.

Beale, N. and Nethercott, S. (1988). Certified sickness in industrial employees threatened with redundancy. *British Medical Journal,* **296, 1508-1510.**

Perspective: epidemiological.
Setting: British small town
References: 18
Type of article/study: Before and after study with a comparison group

Summary: The study was conducted in the small British town of Wiltshire, where the main employer made staged redundancies. Workers fearing job loss reported more illness, and their periods of absence were longer, especially for men and for workers who had previously consulted their general practitioner infrequently. Workers under the age of 40 took less sick leave—perhaps because they feared losing their jobs.

Beard, K.M. and Edwards, J.R. (1995). Employees at risk: contingent work and the psychological

experience of contingent workers. In C.L. Cooper & D.M. Rousseau (Eds.), *Trends in Organizational Behaviour,* Vol.2. Chichester, England: John Wiley and Sons Ltd.

Perspective: organizational behaviour
Setting: n/a
References: 100
Type of article/study: descriptive

Summary: The authors note that there are different and sometimes conflicting perspectives regarding the meaning of contingent work. They adopt the definition of Povlika and Nardone, who define contingent work as "any job in which the individual does not have an explicit or implicit contract for long-term employment or one in which the minimum hours of work can vary in a non-systematic way" (p. 110). Thus contingent and regular work differ in terms of the regularity of on-going employment and the expectation of future employment.

Contingent work is marked by higher job insecurity, lack of retirement or health benefits, few opportunities for advancement within the hiring organization, and, usually, lower pay. Intrinsic features of work such as variety and challenge are usually quite similar between contingent and non-contingent work. Contingent work arrangements are likely to generate or exacerbate perceived job insecurity among contingent workers. Numerous studies have reported that job security is related to various negative outcomes including: lower job satisfaction, reduced career satisfaction and poorer well-being.

Contingent workers are likely to experience low control in several areas. Contingent workers can do little to influence the length of their assignments or control the number of hours that they work (which in turn produces reduced control over income, spending habits, and other lifestyle factors). A considerable amount of research has examined the effects of control on the individual and has generally found that lack of control in the context of work is related to adverse outcomes such as: "reduced job satisfaction, commitment, job involvement, motivation, performance, role stress and mental and physical health" (p. 115). The authors suggest that it is likely that these outcomes would also be prevalent among contingent workers, because contingent work provides little control over the content of work itself as well as the onset and termination of employment.

Contingent workers experience unpredictability in terms of the onset of their employment, the number of hours worked, and the nature of work itself. Studies suggest that low predictability is associated with negative outcomes for the employee, but this evidence is far from conclusive (p. 117). The psychological contract between the contingent worker and his/her employer can be described as transactional and asymmetrical. It is asymmetrical because the employer makes all the decisions concerning the employee's work, and it is transactional because it does not include the type of intrinsic, non-monetary exchanges (e.g. employee works hard in exchange for job security or recognition from the employer) which may arise in more permanent forms of work. There is little empirical evidence that links the form of psychological contract with negative outcomes for employees. However, the authors suggest that it is likely that the transactional and asymmetrical form of contract for those contingent workers who desire more stable employment will likely result in lowered employee contributions and investments, which may be associated with negative work attitudes such as lowered job satisfaction, commitment, job involvement or well-being (p. 118).

Social comparison processes (SCPS) involve the evaluation of oneself against a "referent other" on some relevant dimension. Contingent workers are likely to use permanent workers as their "referent other" since they are likely to work along side them. Contingent workers who work along side permanent workers, may engender in the contingent workers feelings of deprivation or inequity. They may feel deprivation if they compare their level of job security to that of a core worker. Several streams of research suggest that the perception of being disadvantaged as compared to another person is related to various negative outcomes, such as reduced job satisfaction, feelings of injustice, lower employee performance, higher turnover and absenteeism, and increased sickness and accident compensation.

Although using contingent workers may help decrease labour costs, it may hinder productivity and quality due to certain negative outcomes from the psychological experience of contingent work. For example, the reduced commitment experienced by contingent workers may result in lower motivation, productivity and work quality (p.120). Further, lower job involvement has been related to burnout and its associated disengagement from work. The authors suggest that the potential adverse effects on productivity and quality need to be examined before organizations choose to employ significant numbers of contingent workers as a way of improving their operations (p.120).

Beechey, V. and Perkins, T. (1987). A *Matter of Hours: Women, Part Time Work and the Labour Market*. Gloucester: Polity Press.

Perspective: Marxist, feminist
Setting: Britain
References: numerous
Type of article/study: Fieldwork, theoretical framework developed

Summary: Part-time work is overwhelmingly female—over 90% of part time workers in Britain are women. "Most men do full time paid work and very little else, while most women combine paid work with unpaid housework and caring work" (p. 2). Part time work can be characterised by poor status, lack of benefits, high intensity and poor upward mobility.

This research suggests that employers have gender-specific ways of organising their labour force. "When the labour force is female, employers use part-time workers as a means of attaining flexibility. On the other hand, where men are employed, other methods of attaining flexibility are attained" (p.8). In Britain, part time employment is closely correlated with the the employment of married females; in France, however, married women tend to work full-time. [Perhaps due to the availability of affordable day care?]

Binkley, M. (2000) Getting by in tough times: Coping with the fisheries crisis. Working paper. Dalhousie University, Department of Sociology and Social Anthropology. Halifax, Nova Scotia, Canada (Accepted for publication in: *Women's Studies International Forum* 23 (3): 323-332.)

Perspective: social anthropological, economic
Setting: Lunenburg and Halifax counties, Nova Scotia, 1994
References: 8
Type of article/study: qualitative in depth interviews with 25 coastal fisher's wives.

Summary: This paper focuses on the wives of coastal fisherman who live or sail from Lunenburg and Halifax counties, Nova Scotia, Canada. It focuses on the household's attempts to cope—particularly financially—in these changed circumstances. The changing organization of women's work in fishing dependent households is examined in this study. The author specifically notes that "work" in her study is equated with the anthropological sense of livelihood. Sandra Wallman's definition of work is employed in this study: "livelihood is never just a matter of finding or making shelter, transacting money and preparing food to put on the table or exchange in the market place. It is equally a matter of ownership and circulation of information, the management of relationships, the affirmation of personal significance and group identity, and the interrelations of each of these tasks to the other. All these productive tasks together constitute the work of livelihood" (p. 12).

This paper is based on a study of 25 qualitative in-depth tape recorded interviews with coastal fisher's wives. This study was part of a larger project which also included a literature review, a series of in-depth interviews with key informants, a survey of 150 deep sea fisherman's wives and 25 in-depth interviews with deep sea fisherman's wives. In all cases, financial well being had eroded. All employed in this industry had to struggle to develop new ways of meeting the challenges of fishing for a living. For those fishers who still exploited the coastal fishery, their time away from home increased, as they explored more distant waters for fishing purposes. Their wives and families had to cope with their prolonged absences and they had to develop new coping mechanisms to deal with the additional responsibility and autonomy associated with this new lifestyle. More women were going to work or were increasing their work outside the home. Many women were taking on the role of "breadwinner", a task which was not their first choice, and one which was associated with increased stress. Many women still retained their traditional household duties, although some men took on some household chores, most notably lawn mowing, garbage removal and snow shovelling. The decline in wages or the loss of work eroded fishers' self-esteem and aggravated their anxiety. In some cases, this could potentially lead to drinking and family violence. At a macro-level, the restructuring of rural Nova Scotia forces the young and middle aged to move to larger urban centres in search for work, which in turn is associated with a decline in the communities.

Brooker, A.S., Frank, J.W. and Tarasuk, V.S. (1997). Back pain claim rates and the business cycle. *Social Science and Medicine,* 45 (3): 429-439.

Perspective: socio-epidemiological, economic
Setting: Ontario between 1975 and 1993
References: 50
Type of article/study: quantitative ecological study

Summary: This ecological study was conducted in order to shed light on both the etiology and the reporting patterns of back pain claims. Despite the fairly extensive literature on back pain, studies had generally focused on individual-level factors, such as physical or psychological factors, yet there had been little examination of macro-economic factors. The purpose of this study was to fill that gap. In this study, the association between (workers' compensation) back pain claims and the business cycle was tested in Ontario between 1975 and 1993. As a comparison group, a set of claims was created by grouping together 'acute' claims, such as lacerations and fractures. Acute claims were selected as a comparison group, because in contrast to back pain claims, they have a reduced possibility for reporting variation.

The association between age- and sex-adjusted (industry-specific) claim rates and the business cycle, was tested using standard time series analysis, which controlled for auto-correlation, and which de-trended and de-seasonalized the data. Analyses using back pain claim rates and acute claim rates were run separately. Two separate indicators were used for the business cycle: industry-specific unemployment rates and industry-specific total employment rates. The results indicated that both back pain claim rates and acute claim rates increased during expansionary times and decreased during recessionary times.

Furthermore, sub-analyses indicated that this association existed for both men and women and for every ten-year age category. This study refutes the prevalent myth that back pain claims increase during recessionary times (as a way for workers to compensate for job and income insecurity). The results suggest that reporting patterns and/or causal pathways for both occupational back pain and occupational acute injuries appear to have common features, as they relate to the economic climate. Given the current social climate in which back pain claims are viewed suspiciously, this study is important because it shows that back pain claims actually decrease during recessionary times. Two possible explanations may explain the results that were found: (1) during recessionary periods, workers with back pain or acute injuries under-report their injuries, because of fear of lay-offs (2) during expansionary times, increased work pace increases the rate of injuries. This may arise because during periods of economic expansion, average levels of over-time increase, social interaction may be reduced and work-pace may be greater. [It is important to note that although factors such as increased work pace and higher level of over-time may arise during periods of cyclical economic expansion, it is possible that they may also arise as a consequence of structural economic changes—such as restructuring.]

Cahill, J. (1983). Structural characteristics of the macro-economy and mental health: Implications for primary prevention research. *American Journal of Community Psychology*, 11 (5), 553- 571.

Perspective: community psychology
Setting: n/a
References: 82
Type of article/study: descriptive review; the literature pertaining to the five headings listed below, was briefly summarised.

Summary: The article discusses the effect on health of five characteristics of the current economic system (i) instability in the business cycle, (ii) unemployment, (iii) inequality in income distribution, (iv) capital mobility, and (v) fragmentation of the work process. For instance, the authors note that recessionary periods are associated with higher rates of mental illness. Of particular interest is the argument that sudden capital flights and plant closures disrupt the cohesiveness of communities - particularly urban ones (because in urban areas, work serves as a communal function). This article is a good source of references for other studies.

Cameron, S., Horsburgh, M. and Armstrong-Stassen, M. (1994). Effects of downsizing on RNs and RNAs in community hospitals. Working paper #94-6. McMaster University and University of Toronto Quality of Nursing Worklife Research Unit. Hamilton and Toronto.

Perspective: nursing
Setting: Ontario
References: -51
Type of article/study: quantitative and qualitative methods

Summary: The objectives of the study were to determine the quality of work life of registered nurses (RN) and registered nursing assistants (RNA) in community hospitals which were under-going significant reconfiguration plans, which included both major change and downsizing. The research design employed both qualitative and quantitative methods. The quantitative component consisted of a survey administered to about 420 RNs and 150 RNAs. The qualitative component consisted of personal interviews with about 30 individuals.

The research revealed that the practice of nursing within hospital settings has become increasingly diversified. Second, younger RNs who had been in the workforce for a shorter period of time perceived themselves to have less influence in their workplace, less organizational support, and greater job insecurity than older nurses who had been in the workforce longer. In addition they were less satisfied with the kind and amount of work they performed and reported more depersonalization. The study found that RNs and RNAs had different perceptions of what is satisfying or unsatisfying about work, prompting the authors to conclude that these two groups of nurses should be considered as distinct from each other in future research or intervention endeavours. RNs and RNAs who worked full-time and would have preferred to work part-time constituted a particularly high risk group for negative outcomes such as emotional exhaustion and depersonalization. Finally, the last major finding reported by the authors is the lack of satisfaction with supervision that was expressed by both RNs and RNAs.

Catalano, R. and Dooley, D. (1979). Does economic change provoke or uncover behavioural disorder? A preliminary test. Chapter 12 in L.A. Ferman and J.P. Gordus (Eds.) *Mental Health and the Economy.* **Michigan: The WE Upjohn Institute for Employment Research.**

Perspective: economic, social-psychological
Setting: Missouri state, USA
References: n/a (in a book)
Type of article/study: quantitative

Summary: Prior studies had found that admission to mental hospitals was associated with prior macroeconomic change. These studies had been criticized for their failure to identify intervening variables. The purpose of this study was to discriminate between two competing hypotheses. Does economic change serve to uncover existing untreated cases? Or, does it provoke symptoms in individuals who were previously normal? The former hypothesis comes from the life event literature, which implies that major or frequent life changes, particularly undesirable ones, can lead to psychological disequilibrium. Persons with poor coping resources (e.g. social support) may be particularly vulnerable to heightened life changes.

The uncovering explanation, by contrast, suggests that there are a large number of untreated individuals who have psychological symptom levels which are high enough to warrant psychotherapy (the fact that there are large numbers of untreated individuals with psychological symptoms had been found in previous epidemiological surveys). Turbulence in the socio-economic system presumably jars interpersonal relations that define social roles. Family, friends and neighbours may no longer be able to meet social or material needs of the individual because of socio-economic changes. Therefore, the individual may, for the first time, catch the attention of public service gatekeepers such as the police, mental health outreach workers, or social welfare agents. Psychological symptoms of 1,140 respondents were gauged by hour-long personal interviews which covered a variety of health, mental health, life event and demographic variables. Monthly mental health case openings were obtained from the Missouri State Department of Mental Health. Economic variables were ascertained by: the unemployment rate, weighted absolute change of the work force, and absolute change in the size and structure of the work force. Cross-correlation was used to examine the association between the economic and the psychological variables, after de-trending and de-seasonalizing the data. The authors assumed that the uncovering hypothesis would be confirmed if: there was a relationship between economic change and in-patient case openings, no relationship between the incidence of psychological symptoms and in-patient case opening, and a relationship between economic change and inpatient case openings, controlling for symptoms.

The authors assumed that the provocation hypothesis would be confirmed if there was a significant relationship between economic change and inpatient case openings, a significant relationship between symptoms and inpatient case openings, but no relationship between economic change and inpatient case openings, controlling for symptoms. The results suggested that the relationship between economic change and inpatient mental health facilities was due more to the uncovering than to the provocation of behavioural disorders. However, it is a challenge to the uncovering hypothesis to explain why women and the young reacted proportionately to measures of economic well-being (in other words, more favourable economic periods were associated with higher rates of in-patient mental health facilities), while males, the middle-aged and the elderly reacted inversely. The authors suggest that one possible explanation for this finding is that during economic expansion, the perceived need for strong social support within the family may decrease, and thus seeking professional help during this time may be easier for a woman to make. Conversely, tolerance for behavioural problems among men may decrease as the economy heats up.

Christenson, K. (1989). Women and contingent work. In D. Eitzen & M.B. Zinn (Eds.), The *Reshaping of America: Social Consequences of the Changing Economy* **(pp.73-80). Englewood Cliffs, NJ: Prentice Hall. (Originally from an article in Social Policy, 1987.)**

Perspective: sociological
Setting: USA
References: 20
Type of article/study: descriptive

Summary: Christensen points out that the term 'contingent work' as currently being used, refers to a multitude of arrangements such as: alterations in the amount of time on the job, alternative contractual agreements (such as working as an independent contractor), and altering the place of work (such as working at home). For the purposes of her article, she uses contingent work to refer to: part time work, temporary work and independent contracting. The US Department of Labour estimates that the majority of American women work because of human need. Approximately two thirds of working women are widowed, divorced, separated, have never been married, or have husbands whose annual income is less than $15,000 a year. The majority of women work in jobs that are lower paying and offer limited opportunity for advancement. Structural changes in the American economy include: competition from abroad, technology, and the transformation of the American economy from industrial to service sector. These changes affect the design, structure and nature of jobs in the USA. For instance, there is increasing use of independent contractors doing work which formerly would have been by in-house employees. The author suggests that many companies may be hiring these 'independent' contractors fraudulently, as common law suggests that independent contracting status is achieved when workers have control over the nature or pacing of the work, and have the opportunity of incurring profit or loss. If the worker exercises minimal control and has no real opportunity to gain or lose, that worker should likely be an employee and eligible for all benefits given to employees, rather than a self-employed independent contractor. Employer advantages to contingent work are noted: cost containment, flexible staffing, and avoiding unions. Employee disadvantages include: lack of fringe benefits (lack of pensions is particularly troubling for women, an area where women are already vulnerable), lack of advancement opportunities, and difficulty of moving from contingent work back into the 'core' of the corporation. Employee advantages include: flexibility of schedule for women with families, and the fact that sometimes contingent work is better than nothing when women cannot find full time employment.

Cox, R. W. (1994). Global restructuring: Making sense of the changing international political economy. In R .Stubbs and G.R.D. *Underhill. Political Economy and the Changing Global Order. New York: St. Martin's Press.*

Perspective: political economy
Setting: global
References: 23
Type of article/study: descriptive

Summary: A popular new form of production is post-Fordism which is based on economies of flexibility in which there is a relatively small core of permanent employees and a larger pool of temporary workers. Restructuring into the core-periphery model has facilitated the use of a more precariously employed labour force segmented by ethnicity, gender, nationality or religion. It has also made business less controllable by any single state authority. Further, it has weakened the power of trade unions and strengthened that of capital.

Dekker, S. W. A. and Schaufeli, W. B. (1995). The effects of job insecurity on psychological health and withdrawal: A longitudinal study. *Australian Psychologist,* 30(1): 57-63.

Perspective: psychological, organizational behaviour
Setting: large Australian public transport organization
References: 39
Type of article/study: self-report survey with repeat measures (longitudinal)

Summary: This paper reports on a repeated measures study (with two month follow up) of job insecurity which was conducted during a period of drastic organizational change in one of Australia's large public transport organizations. At the start of the study, all participants were in departments in which there was uncertainty about the continuation of their operations. The 'axe fell' in two of the four departments during the course of the study. Thus serendipitously, the four departments split up into a redundant group (n=32) and a control group (n=63).

Results indicated that job insecurity is associated with a deterioration of psychological health (leading to psychological stress and burnout), as well as job and organizational withdrawal. Insecurity and its associated effects on health decreased in the group of employees that had been made redundant and partly redeployed. By contrast, the control group of continuously employed workers experienced an increase in job insecurity, more symptoms of psychological stress and burnout and greater withdrawal from the job and the organization over the same time period. It appears from the study that certainty about a job situation (even if that means being made redundant) is less detrimental to a worker's psychological health than a situation of prolonged job insecurity. However, the results could also be explained by the fact that redundant employees were given a modest 'golden handshake' which may have alleviated the stress of financial burden on the redundant employees. Contrary to the expectations of the investigators, neither support from colleagues nor unions seemed to protect job incumbents from the negative effects of job insecurity. However, that result is tentative due to the small sample size and thus the weak power of the statistical test. Further, another possible explanation for that finding is that employees experiencing high levels of psychological stress may be more likely to seek social support. Nonetheless, the authors conclude that in order to combat the adverse effects of job insecurity on psychological health and morale, the job stressor has to be dealt with directly, rather than trying to render it less harmful by providing more social support.

Duffy, A. and Pupo, N. (1992). *Part-Time Paradox: Connecting Gender, Work and Family.* **Toronto, Ontario: McClelland and Stewart Inc.**

Perspective: social psychological, sociology of work, work-family
Setting: Canada, with international comparison
References: -600
Type of article/study: conceptual, review of Canadian and international statistical data, and qualitative interviews with 70 part-time women workers in southern Ontario.

Summary: The book takes a detailed look at part-time work, particularly with respect to women, who comprise three-quarters of Canada's two million part-time workers. The authors discuss issues of women, work and family and offer a statistical profile of part time work, with historical and international comparisons. One chapter is devoted to laying out various different theoretical perspectives used in understanding women's participation in part-time work. The various dimensions of part-time work (eg working conditions, wages and benefits, advantages/disadvantages for employers and employees) are discussed, as is the role of unions in part-time work issues. The empirical qualitative data is used to describe the experiences of part-time women workers and the significance of this form of work for their lives, particularly their efforts to balance work and family commitments. The book projects into the future and reflects on the transformations taking place in the Canadian and global economies, and on the possibility that part-time work will continue to be a marginalized and poorly paid sector of the work force. Health implications are not considered apart from a section (p.127-129) dealing with some of the mental health effects of part-time work for women. Useful appendices identify and define a range of 'new' forms of work and what is known about their prevalence.

Earnshaw, A.R., Amundson, N.E. and Borgen, W.A. (1990). The experience of job insecurity for professional women. *Journal of Employment Counselling,* **27 (March): 2-18.**

Perspective: psychological, counselling
Setting: Vancouver, Canada
References: 44
Type of article/study: qualitative

Summary: This article presents the results of a qualitative study which described the experience of professional women threatened with job insecurity. Twenty professional women, with at least bachelor degrees, aged 23 to 49 years, were given focused interviews of 55 to 70 minutes in length. The women had job insecurity which ranged from a few weeks to 5 years or more. Ten participants were married (six with children), four were divorced and single parents, six were single. The interview was focused on these areas: the impact of job insecurity on work and work relations, leisure and home life, financial concerns, health and future expectations. Within this framework, participants were free to provide the information, thoughts and feelings that they considered relevant to their job insecurity. The tapes of the interviews, life-line drawings, and complete, coded transcripts formed the data base for the analysis. The method of analysis followed the scheme suggested by Spradley (1979). Reliability checks of the analysis was performed by colleagues familiar with interview analysis, but not with this research topic. In general, the interviews painted a picture of disillusionment, loss of trust, low morale, sense of personal isolation and pessimism about the future world of work. These women were making the best of a bad situation but their aim was eventually to land a job with a permanent rate of pay, tenure and benefits.

Throughout the women's accounts, several themes emerged consistently from the data, namely: loss of identity, investment or disinvestment, powerlessness and the struggle for control, betrayal of expectations, grieving and renewal. The authors note that these themes indicate the values symbolized by society regarding paid employment. Such values as status, autonomy, creative endeavour, and the opportunity for career advancement were important for these women and their threatened loss was a major component of job insecurity. The effects on emotional and physical health, as reported by participants were as follows: stress and tension (n=17), anxiety (n=15), feeling depressed (n=13), loss of energy, drive (n=12), irritability, short temper (n=9), disturbed sleep pattern (n=8), seeking medical attention (n=8), increase in colds, flus, allergies (n=7), muscle tension, back problems (n=7), increase in headaches, migraines (n=7), disturbed eating pattern (n=6), weeping (n=6), poor concentration (n=6), feeling chronically stressed (n=5). The authors suggest that an area of particular interest would be a critical comparison of these factors using larger samples of both men and women, and in different occupational categories.

Ferrie, J.E., Shipley, M.J., Marmot, M.G., Stansfeld, S. and Davey Smith, G. (1998). **The health effects of major organizational change and job insecurity.** *Social Science and Medicine* 46 (2): 243-254.

Perspective: epidemiological
Setting: London-based office staff in 20 civil service departments between 1985 and 1988
References: 64
Type of article/study: prospective, quantitative follow-up study

Summary: In the UK since 1988, an increasing proportion of the executive functions of government in the UK have been devolved to executive agencies. Transfer to an executive agency involves a period of uncertainty during which the options of elimination or transfer to the private sector are considered, followed by a marked change in management style and further periods of uncertainty when the agency's function is reconsidered for transfer to the private sector. This study examines the effect of this major organizational change and subsequent job insecurity on the health status of a cohort of 7419 white-collar civil servants by comparing groups either exposed to or anticipating exposure to this stressor with controls experiencing no change. Data were gathered longitudinally at three periods of time over an eight year period (1985-1993). During the first period of the first survey, data were gathered during a period of stable employment well before any indication of change. Compared with controls, men already working in and anticipating transfer to an executive agency experienced significant self-reported increases in longstanding illnesses, adverse sleep patterns, mean number of symptoms in the fortnight before questionnaire completion and minor psychiatric morbidity. Significant relative increases in body mass index were seen in both exposure groups while exposure to agency status was also associated with significant relative increases in blood pressure. Health-related behaviours tended to favour those in the exposure groups.

Compared with controls, women in both exposure groups reported small increases in most self-reported morbidity measures and most clinical measurements, accompanied by slight beneficial changes in some health-related behaviours and small adverse changes in others. Significant relative increases were seen in mean number of symptoms, in ischaemia among women anticipating exposure, and in body mass index among those exposed to agency status. The adverse trends cannot be explained by changes in the health damaging behaviours measured among the men and probably not among the women, despite a small increase in such behaviours among the latter.

Compared to women, men exhibited greater increases in self-reported physical and psychological morbidity than women, and these changes were generally statistically significant, while the changes were generally not statistically significant for women. The authors refer to other studies and suggest that this finding may relate to the fact that for women, factors outside the workplace, including partner' class and employment status and material conditions in which the household lives may be particularly important, and that self-reported health for women is less closely related to their own occupational class and employment status than it is for men. Further, domestic responsibilities and caring have also been shown to be important determinants of women's self-reported morbidity.

The changes that were found in this study, although often significant for men, were quite small, with Odds Ratios (OR) from 1.2 to 1.6. The authors suggest that the effect of organizational change on health and health related behaviours is likely under-estimated in this study, as the control group was also exposed to the general changes that took place in the civil service between 1979 and the time of the final questionnaire, with the exception of transfer to an executive agency.

François, M. (1994). Précarisation de l'emploi, précarité du travail. XXXIIIes *Journées nationales de médecine du travail,* **Besançon, France.**

Perspective: occupational health and safety
Setting: France, OECD
References: 19
Type of article/study: descriptive [Note: This article is in French]

Summary: The beginning of the 1970s saw the emergence of new forms of employment. The authors note that 'precarious' employment is defined as it relates to typical employment - the latter is characterised by unlimited duration, full-time, and with a single employer. [Note: we use precarious as the translation to their word "récarité".] Employment which diverges from this standard is considered precarious employment. Statistics from the OECD suggest that precarious employment will exceed 10% of salaried employment. Of the 10.3% of the unemployed population in France, 41% are people who have completed contracts of fixed length, or who have arrived at the end of an interim contract. Estimates are also given of the proportion of the population engaged in fixed term contracts, part time work, home work, and black market work. Non-traditional forms of work arrangements are held disproportionately by the young, the poorly qualified, and women (p.173). The authors note that on the basis of available studies, workers in "precarious" employment are subject to elevated risks compared to permanent workers. Studies by Broda, François and Liévin have demonstrated that in the chemical and metallurgical sectors, dangerous positions were frequently given to interim workers employed directly by the workplace in question, or by an intermediary company. The result was that these interim workers had more than twice the frequency of accidents. Another study (conducted by L'Institut National de la Santé et de la Recherche Médicale) found that temporary workers—interim or short term contract—in the nuclear industry had elevated doses of ionizing radiation (p.175).

Gottfried H. (1992). In the margins: Flexibility as a mode of regulation in the temporary help service industry. *Work, Employment and Society*, 6 (3),443-460.

Perspective: sociological, labour process and feminist theory
Setting: medium-sized US city
References: 48
Type of article/study: participant observation study in which the researcher worked as a temporary service worker. The data were supplemented with 18 open-ended interviews with temporary clerical workers.

Summary: A major theme of this article is the control of labour. The authors note that most studies discuss control in the context of the standard industrial model. Temporary Help Service (THS) industry workers, although they differ from manufacturing workers in terms of spatial and temporal characteristics, are still subject to control, although this control takes on a slightly different form. The control of THS workers comes from both the THS firm and the client-firm where the THS worker is placed. As an example of the control from the THS firm, employees are subject to standardized tests, and are given rules for on-the-job behaviour (e.g. dress codes and supervisory protocol) which the employee must follow in the absence of direct management. At the placement site, control is exerted by keeping the THS worker physically detached from other workers, and sometimes by the use of computer-based technologies which can closely monitor workers. Firms can also use THS workers as a form of control for their permanent employees, by implicitly threatening to substitute contingent workers in place of core ones. THS firms emphasise the importance of proper feminine attire during work assignments, thus symbolically constituting the temporary clerical worker as a gendered subject. Further, they principally hire women due to their assumption that women will accept flexible labour due to their responsibility for reproductive household labour.

Temporary workers have little or no discretionary time on the job. As a result, they may well put in more time on-the-job than permanent workers, since they don't engage in non-productive activities such as chatting in the hall or taking coffee breaks. Furthermore, it is hard for THS workers to manage their time off-the-job. They must stay close to the phone in anticipation of work assignments and one THS firm even has a policy of dismissing workers who refuse three consecutive assignments, or who fail to contact the counsellor within 48 hours of completing an assignment. "THS workers are close to being the reserve army of labour, are subordinate to two or more organizations, are recruited to perform 'deskilled work' and are predominantly women" (p. 448). The authors note that the use of "flexible" workers is a means of achieving greater capital accumulation and worker regulation through marginalisation. Between 1963 and 1979, THS employment increased by 725% compared with only 58% in nonagricultural jobs in the USA. There are no references to health effects in this article.

Hakim, C. (1995). Workforce restructuring in cross-national perspective. Review Article.

Employment and Society, 9 (2): 379-388.

Perspective:Europe, sociological & economic, generally atheoretical
Setting: Europe
References: 10
Type of article/study: review article

Summary: Provides a review of five European reports/articles that describe European labour market trends. This article offers a good starting point for anyone interested in European labour market trends, but has limited direct applicability to the topic of restructuring and women's health.

Hartley, J. (1991). **Industrial relations and job insecurity: A social psychological framework** . In J. Hartley, D. Jacobson, B. Klandermans and T. van Vuuren (Eds.), *Job Insecurity: Coping With Jobs at Risk* (pp 104-122). Newbury Park, CA: Sage Publications.

Perspective: social-psychological and industrial relations
Setting: n/a
References: -30
Type of article/study: conceptual

Summary: Hartley proposes that a social psychological framework is essential to understanding some of the changes which have been taking place in industrial relations. The author examines some of the existing macro-economic and institutional literature on industrial relations and organizational restructuring and suggests that job insecurity is a valuable intervening variable to explain industrial-relations attitudes and behaviour. The author puts forward a framework which acknowledges the economic and organizational constraints within which industrial relations take place but also gives due attention to subjective interpretations of reality in industrial relations. The author concludes that: "Job insecurity has been identified as one variable which is implicit but unexplored in the literature on industrial relations. The impact of job insecurity is explored here both for its impact on individual attitudes and behaviours and for its influence on collective behaviour" (p.122).

Hartley, J. (1991). **Industrial Relations and Job Insecurity: Learning from a Case Study.** In: J. Hartley, D. Jacobson, B. Klandermans and T. van Vuuren (Eds.), *Job Insecurity: Coping With Jobs at Risk* (pp 123-150). Newbury Park, CA: Sage Publications.

Perspective: social psychological and industrial relations.
Setting: a company in Britain
References: -20
Type of article/study: a case study

Summary: The study was based on a single organization during a period of "decline." The data consisted of a questionnaire sample of 137 predominantly manual workers (response rate of 42%), over 100 interviews with 51 people across all functions and levels, and an intensive six week period of observation, including attendance at union and union-management meetings.

The study revealed that job insecurity was associated with a number of opinions and beliefs, such as trust in management and industrial-relations climate. However, a number of propositions suggested by the author in the previous chapter (see above item) were not supported by the data. The degree of involvement in union affairs was not clearly related to job insecurity. From the interview data, the period of upheaval and uncertainty made workers somewhat less keen to be directly involved in union work and more cautious as shop stewards. Job insecurity played a key role in the intertwining of insecurity, trust, industrial-relations climate and on-going union-management relations. A significant relationship existed between insecurity and trust: insecure workers trusted management less. Trust is known to be critical to good industrial relations, and to co-operation and adaptation. In this case, conflict between management and union intensified even though both parties were weakened through their dependencies with each other. Unions were dependent on management for the continuation of jobs, and management was dependent on the unions for co-operation to maintain production. The author concludes by arguing that it is insufficient to analyse industrial relations only at the institutional level. Analyses conducted solely at this level have failed to explain what has happened during periods of recessions and restructuring. Attitudinal data are essential in order to understand the effects of recession and other more general economic change.

Heaney, C.A., Israel, B.A., and House, J.S. (1994). Chronic job insecurity among automobile workers: effects on job satisfaction and health. *Social Science and Medicine* 38 (10): 1431-1437.

Perspective: social epidemiology
Setting: automobile manufacturing workers in a mid-sized city in the USA
References: 28
Type of article/study: survey

Summary: A longitudinal self-administered survey of 207 automobile manufacturing workers in a single organization was conducted at two distinct time periods in April 1986 (Time 1) and again in June 1987 (Time 2). The purpose of the study was to investigate the effects of job insecurity on lack of job satisfaction and physical symptoms. A six-item scale measured job satisfaction. Physical symptomatology was assessed by an index of 17 somatic symptoms including: shortness of breath or trouble breathing; chest tightness, pressure and pain; "racing" or pounding heart; frequent colds or sore throats; persistent coughs; cramps or pain in the hands, wrists, arms, back and legs; eye strain and eye irritation; ringing in the ears; difficulty hearing; skin irritation; and frequent headaches. Both a Time 2 level of job insecurity and a chronically high level at both Time 1 and Time 2 were predictive of decreases in job satisfaction. For physical health however, a chronic high level of job insecurity was the best predictor of increases in symptomatology. Chronically high job insecurity was not related to Time 2 depressive symptoms, suggesting that negative affectivity does not account for the study results. This is especially pertinent because the importance of negative affectivity as a confounder in stress research is currently being hotly debated, and empirical evidence from other studies has shown inconsistent results. In addition, in-depth interviews with a subset of study participants portrayed job insecurity as a major stressor in this plant for the past ten years. Since job insecurity existed to some extent before the start of the study, the size of the effects of chronic job insecurity on job satisfaction and physical symptoms may be under-estimated. The employees in this study had worked for this company for an average of almost 20 years; further, it would be difficult for these employees to find a new job that would match the wage and benefit packages of their current job. Thus, the findings may differ for workers with much shorter job tenure and/or who could easily find jobs comparable to those that they had just lost.

International Lady Garment Workers' Union. (1993). *Homeworkers Survey: Summary of Findings.* **Working Paper. Toronto, Ontario.**

Perspective: Labour
Setting: Metropolitan Toronto area
Type of study: in-depth interviews with 45 immigrant women who sew clothes in their homes.
References: none

Summary: The report reveals the extreme exploitation experienced by the women who make up this sector of the workforce in the garment industry. Homeworkers are not subject to the same type of legislative protection as other workers, and even the legal rights they do have seem not to be adhered to. Over 60% of the sample work below the minimum wage, and a majority of the sample (56%) reported that their piece-rates had decreased. Although home workers are entitled to vacation pay, 87% reported that they were not receiving vacation pay. None of the homeworkers had employers that were paying Canadian Pension Plan or Employment Insurance on their behalf. The women who had recently become homeworkers reported that their factory wage had been $4.00/hour more than their current wage. A majority of respondents stated that they would prefer to work outside the home. Homeworkers have little control over their work schedule, many of them (44%) report having problems with employers. Regarding health and safety problems, 95% of the homeworkers reported back strain, 91% reported stress (e.g. from having to finish the work quickly), 73% identified allergies problems related to fabric dust, and 85% reported concern over eye strain.

All homeworkers reported that they take care of their children during their work time, with 91% reporting that they became homeworkers because they became pregnant and needed child care while working, and that lack of affordable and/or acceptable day care was a factor in their decision to do home work.

Jenkins, R. , MacDonald, A., Murray, J. and Strathdee, G. (1982). Minor psychiatric morbidity and the threat of redundancy in a professional group. *Psychological Medicine,* **12: 799-807.**

Perspective: epidemiological
Setting: British newspaper
References: 31
Type of article/study: exploratory quantitative study with repeat prevalence measures over a period of six months.

Summary: After the journalists of a national newspaper had been issued with redundancy notices, a prospective study was carried out to determine the effect of the threat of their redundancy on minor psychiatric morbidity. The most common symptoms displayed by the sample were complaints of poor sleep (60% of cases), depression (47% of cases), and fatigue (43% of cases). Anxiety, poor concentration, and irritability were also some fairly common complaints. Following the subsequent withdrawal of redundancy notices, there was considerable reduction in minor psychiatric morbidity. The results of the study are tentative due to the small sample size and the exploratory nature of the study. The authors conclude by suggesting numerous improvements in their method for subsequent studies.

Kozlowski, S.W.J., Chao, G.T., Smith, E.M. and Hedlund, J. (1993). **Organizational downsizing: strategies, interventions, and research implications.** *International Review of Industrial and Organizational Psychology,* 8, 263- 332.

Perspective: psychological
Setting: n/a
References: -360
Type of article/study: review

Summary: This review summarizes studies that relate to organizational downsizing. The prevalence of downsizing, macro theories of organizational evolution, micro descriptions of downsizing, the effects of downsizing (on those who lost their jobs as well as the survivors) and the management of the process of downsizing are all comprehensively reviewed and critiqued in this article. This summary focuses exclusively on the literature relating to the effects of downsizing on the surviving personnel. One study of downsizing found that while management expected individuals to handle increased responsibility and decision-making in a downsized organization, employees reported significant increases in role conflict, role ambiguity, and role overload, and a decrease in positive feedback following downsizing. Another study found that the uncertainty and disruption associated with restructuring was positively related to employee stress. Restructuring is sometimes associated with job relocation. Studies seems to indicate that individuals with fewer family ties and who have friends or highly esteemed co-workers who have decided to transfer may be more likely to transfer to a new location. Individuals who are demoted are likely to suffer from a salary reduction and may also experience negative self-attitudes and a decreased commitment to the organization. Surviving employees who see their fellow workers and friends being laid off may experience decreased morale and commitment to the organization. However, research suggests that survivors can react positively or negatively to the layoff depending on the perceived fairness of the layoff procedure. [The authors do not discuss any findings in this section that relate particularly to the experience of women. Thus we do not know whether that was an over-sight on the part of the authors or whether there is a paucity of research on women in this area.]

Kuhl, J. (1990). *New Deal and New Forms of Employment.* International Institute for Labour Studies. Geneva: International Labour Organization.

Perspective: labour
Setting: Europe
References: 32
Type of article/study: descriptive

Summary: This paper describes new forms of employment that have flexible wages and adaptable employment. "Contingent" workers are characterised especially by insecurity, although a contract exists which defines the task for a limited duration. Most people recruited in this way are excluded from the protection of general labour legislation. "Life-of-the-project" workers are employed as long as the projects concerned exist. "Fake" self-employment workers include one person companies in a dependency situation based on subcontracting. In all EC countries there is a trend towards the transformation of salaried employees into self-employed workers who often continue to work for their original employer. Further, there are linkages between self-employment and black market activities. Other trends in Europe include a decline in unit labour costs since 1982 and the fact that total hours worked did not grow in the EC in the 1980s.

Kuhnert, KW, Sims, R. & Lahey, M. (1989). **The relationship between job security and employee health.** *Group and Organization Studies,* 14 (4): 399-410.

Perspective: organizational behaviour, industrial psychology
Setting: two manufacturing organizations in the northeastern USA
References: 28
Type of article/study: survey of 201 employees

Summary: The majority of respondents were line workers, and about half of the respondents were female. Both job security and health measures were based on employees' self-reports. In both organizations studied, a global measure of job security was significantly related to a global measure of employee health, while decreased job security was related to greater symptoms of ill-health. While both organizations yielded a significant correlation between health and job security, the relationship between the constructs was different between the two companies. The study suggests that organizational structure, climate and culture may moderate the relationship between job security and outcomes.

Leach, B. and Winson, A. (1995). **Bringing "globalization" down to earth: Restructuring and labour in rural communities.** *The Canadian Review of Sociology and Anthropology,* 32 (3): 341-364.

Perspective: sociological—linking of macro trends with micro-level experiences.
Setting: a rural county in Southern Ontario (North Wellington). The authors note that their study is an attempt to fill the void with respect to research on the rural dimension of corporate restructuring in the Canadian context.
References: 41
Type of article/study: ethnographic case study of former plant workers, discussed in relation to the nature of contemporary Canadian capitalism.

Summary: Many of the observed trends at the "macro" (state, system) level were confirmed in their study at the "micro" (community, family, individual) level. These macro-level trends include increasing labour flexibility (e.g. cheaper wage bills), contingent work, two-tiered wage structure, increasing wage inequality, increasing proportion of Canadians experiencing long-term unemployment, and the development of sharp inter-regional differences in the duration of unemployment in the most recent recession.

Restructuring has meant a substantial drop in income for those in their rural Ontario sample, even for those who were successful at gaining re-employment. For those who did find new work, it was usually part-time contingent work or work for substantially lower pay in a non-union shop. In the rural economies that they studied, there was little evidence of the "good jobs" that some writers argue are associated with the new information economy. Men were more likely to find equally skilled work than women—albeit with a commute of 50 to 80 km. For many women, entering more distant labour markets was not an option because of children or other family responsibilities. Older workers as a group found it particularly difficult to seek re-employment. Financial distress placed a strain on family relationships, causing a number of short term or permanent family break-ups. No links with health are presented in this article, but the rural perspective is interesting.

Lewchuk, W. & Robertson, D. (1997). Production without empowerment: Work reorganization from the perspective of motor vehicle workers. *Capital & Class* 63 (Autumn): 37-64.

Perspective: work organization, labour
Setting: Canadian vehicle assembly departments of CAMI, Chrysler, Ford and General Motors
References: 39
Type of article/study: survey of workers

Summary: Background. The Fordist model of work organization is characterised by limited involvement of individual workers in decision making. Recent work by Karasek and Theorell have found that Fordist-type jobs with high demands and low decision latitude are associated with stress-related heart diseases. The 'Ford Flu', noted by Detroit doctors in the 1930s, was defined as illness brought on by the unique combination of heavy workloads, severe job insecurity, and limited control over the pace and rhythm of work. However, as long as the Fordist system was assumed to be a more efficient way of producing goods, the calls for change and for humanizing the labour process went largely unheeded. It is now widely believed that in order to remain competitive, organizations need to implement more flexible forms of work organization. 'Lean production' is characterised by: (1) design of products with an eye towards manufacturability, (2) use of more flexible machinery, (3) reorganization of the manufacturing process to reduce inventories and improve product flows, and (4) reorganization of work to make better use of labour's knowledge of the production process. In addition, the promoters of lean production also claim that better use of worker knowledge about the production process will lead to worker empowerment which will provide a solution to the social problems associated with Fordism. The research question of this study was: do new forms of work organization enhance individual worker control over their immediate work environment in a way that allows them to enhance the quality of their working life? The study consisted of three components, with the survey being the primary component: (1) a survey which was distributed randomly to approximately one out of every 6 production workers (n=2,424), (2) a site visit which included the inspection of the production process and interviews with members of the union executive and (3) a review of company documents. Overall, the study found little evidence that motor vehicle workers were empowered. The majority surveyed found it difficult to modify their jobs, vary their work-pace, or leave their station to attend to personal matters. Direct production workers at lean plants continued to have little scope to change things they did not like about their jobs, often found it difficult to vary the rhythm of work, often found it difficult to get time off to attend to personal matters and had a workload which left little time for resting during a job cycle.

The authors present their results in table format, dichotomised by the gender of the respondent, and by employer. For the most part, differences between men and women were relatively small, and comparisons between men and women is difficult given that women comprised only 12% of the entire sample. There is evidence in this paper that at lean plants, managerial control of workers has actually increased. A careful reading of various company documents revealed that the real focus in lean production is process control. The authors conclude by suggesting that instead of solving the social and health problems associated with Fordism, lean production may actually compound them.

Marcotte, R.W. (1995). Declining job stability: what we know and what it means. *Journal of Policy Analysis and Management* **14 (4): 590-598.**

Perspective: policy analysis
Setting: USA
References: 20
Type of article/study: descriptive

Summary: This article describes how job stability has fallen substantially for workers without any college education and for black workers. Furthermore, these changes preceded the recent recession by at least a decade. The trends identified in the research raise a number of policy issues relating to how workers whose careers involve more job changing and less job security can be assured economic security.

Martinus, L., Royle, L., Boblin-Cummings, S., Baumann, A., Oolup, P., Smith, S. and Blythe, J. (1995). Exploring the effects of change on nurse practice in acute ambulatory settings: A qualitative study. Working paper 95-10. Hamilton University and the University of Toronto Quality of Nursing Worklife Research Unit. Hamilton and Toronto.

Perspective: nursing, sociological
Setting: three different acute ambulatory care settings in a major Canadian teaching hospital that had recently experienced downsizing.
Type of article/study: qualitative individual and focus group interviews and grounded theory analysis methodology.
References: 36

Summary: Downsizing affected the totality of nurses' working lives including: work environment, nursing roles, job satisfaction and interpersonal relations with others. One of the most persistent themes to emerge from the data was the intensification of work that occurred as a result of downsizing. Nurses noted that there was an increase in the number of patients requiring care, and yet they had a diminished work force to deal with them. The increased intensification of their workload, combined with the lack of adequate response to these demands from their workplace resulted in greater levels of stress among the nurses. Individual stress was apparent in reports of tiredness, irritability with colleagues and lack of self care evidenced by failure to take breaks.

Mattera, P. (1989). Home computer sweat shops. In D. S. Eitzen and M.B. Zinn (Eds.). *The Reshaping of America: Social Consequences of the Changing Economy* **(pp. 319-323). Englewood Cliffs, NJ: Prentice Hall, (Originally from an article in** *The Nation,* **1983).**

Perspective: labour perspective, sociological, some class and gender consideration
Setting: USA

References: none
Type of article/study: descriptive/journalistic

Summary: Mattera starts the article by describing the day in the life of a claims worker for Blue Cross. For fifty hours of work in a week the worker makes a mere $5,000/year (in about 1983).
From the employer perspective, home workers are a cost saving - as benefits are rarely provided and the effects of absenteeism and tardiness are virtually eliminated. Further, pay tends to be much lower for home workers. Some employers like to portray themselves as socially responsible, and they portray working at home as a boon to the handicapped and those who cannot travel to work. However, some employers are weary of an arrangement in which they lose the ability to supervise, even despite strict controls. Mattera notes that unions have called home work a union-busting technique, because none of the current home workers are unionized. Home working is a way that unionized companies can ship out their work to non-unionized suppliers. From the employee perspective, working at home has many disadvantages. Working at home means isolation and restricted socializing and informal cooperation - aspects of work that can mitigate the negative experience of low skill clerical work. Home work is also a convenient way for employers to shift overhead to the worker and to evade demands for decent pay and benefits. The author points out that it is
    crucial to consider notions of class and gender when examining home work. Some futurologists embrace the notion of working at home, and predict that it will lead people to become more involved in their communities. However, the advantages of working at home for the upper middle class may not exist for the lower class. Being at home without money can be like living in a prison. Furthermore, the isolation of home work can be disempowering, and deprive women of the social status that working with others provides. Mattera points out that the new right has embraced home work as a means to strengthen the nuclear family. He concludes with a suggestion that labour and women's movements should start to address the problem of home workers, and, more specifically, to decide whether they should they seek a ban on home work or try to organize home workers.

Mattiason, I., Lingarde, F., Nilsson, J.A. and Theorell, T. (1990). Threat of unemployment and cardiovascular risk factors: Longitudinal study of quality of sleep and serum cholesterol concentrations in men threatened with redundancy. *British Medical Journal,* 301, 461-466.

Perspective: epidemiological
Setting: study of male shipyard workers in Sweden
References: 26
Type of article/study: longitudinal study with a comparison group over the same period

Summary: The aim of this study was to determine whether a relationship existed between the threat of job loss and changes in risk factors for cardiovascular disease. Secondly, the investigators wanted to determine whether mental stress and sleep disturbance were related to and might explain the possible changes in risk factors for cardiovascular disease.
The study group consisted of 715 male workers at a shipyard in Malmo, Sweden who were given notice about the closure of their shipyard. The control group consisted of a random sample of Malmo residents (n=261), comparable with the study population with regard to age, screening history and duration of follow up. Data were obtained from health screening examinations that were performed at the Malmo General Hospital. As most of the study group had attended earlier screening examinations at the hospital

(and prior to the announcement of the shipyard closure), the study thus had a series of observations over time which allowed the investigators to examine the impact of the shipyard closure on the variables measured. The investigators found that the risk of unemployment increased the serum cholesterol concentration (a risk factor for cardiovascular disease) in middle aged men, the increase being more pronounced in those with sleep disturbances and immigrants, and almost non-existent among men who were offered early retirement on full pay. Men with increased serum cholesterol concentrations also manifested increases in other established risk factors for cardiovascular disease. The authors conclude that their findings may partly explain the high mortality in conjunction with unemployment and sleep disturbance which has been reported in earlier epidemiological studies.

Mayhew, C. and Quinlan, M. (1998). *Outsourcing and Occupational Health and Safety: A Comparative Study of Factory-Based and Outworkers in the Australian TCF Industry.* **Sydney, Australia: UNSW (University of New South Wales) Studies in Australian Industrial Relations.**

Perspective: industrial relations, occupational health and safety
Setting: Australia
References: 195
Type of article/study: extensive literature review; empirical survey.

Summary: In this study 100 factory-based workers and 100 out-workers in the clothing manufacturing industry were interviewed face to face and assisted in answering a detailed questionnaire. The shift from factory based employment to out-working in Australia has occurred because of changes in tariff protection, the increasing concentration of retail ownership, and the 1990s recession. It has been estimated that only between 1 in 14 or 1 in 20 Australian textile/clothing workers are employed in factories. Compared to factory workers, out-worker employees are more likely to be recent immigrants. The associated deterioration in occupational health and safety (OHS) is hidden because the injuries and illnesses of out-workers do not appear in compensation statistics. The occupational health and safety status of out-workers was found to be unequivocally and significantly worse than those of factory workers. The out-worker market niche entails intensive production to meet a series of short cycle demand requirements with tight deadlines. The result is intensive work with tight deadlines. Soft tissue injuries were more common among out-workers than factory workers (e.g. 27% and 10% annual incidence ratio respectively), as were chronic injuries (79% vs 34%) and occupational violence 49% with verbal abuse among out-workers, and virtually none among factory-based workers. This article is also noteworthy for its very thorough literature review.

Neis, B. (1995). Can't get my breath: Snow crab workers' occupational asthma. In K. Messing, B. Neis and L. Dumais (Eds.), *Invisible: Issues in Women's Occupational Health/La Santé des Travailleuses* **(pp 3-28). Charlottetown, P.E.I.: Gynergy Books.**

Perspective: occupational health, institutional response
Setting: Quebec and Newfoundland and Labrador
References: 46
Type of Article/study: comparative case study
Summary: One consequence of the collapse of the groundfish stocks in Atlantic Canada has been a

restructuring of fisheries in the region in the direction of snow crab and shrimp. There are occupational health risks associated with this restructuring and most snow crab processing workers are women. This comparative case study investigates the identification and institutional responses to snow crab occupational asthma in the two provinces of Quebec and Newfoundland and Labrador. Although some of the first research on snow crab asthma was carried out in Newfoundland, there has been little pubic recognition of this occupational disease and no organized effort to either study it or minimize incidence. Institutional response has taken the form of secondary rather than primary prevention and workers with symptoms appear to have limited access to health professionals with adequate training in occupational asthma. Affected workers often continue to work, relying on the seasonality of the industry and medication to manage their symptoms. In Quebec, in contrast, institutional response to the discovery of snow crab asthma produced research and primary-prevention related initiatives. These appear to have significantly reduced incidence in that province.

Novek, J., Yassi, A. and Spiegel, J. (1989). Mechanization, the labor process, and injury risks in the Canadian meat packing industry. *International Journal of Health Services,* **20 (2): 281-296.**

Perspective: labour, occupational health and safety
Setting: Canada, meat packing industry, 1980s
References: 52

Summary: During the 1980's, Canada's manufacturing industries experienced considerable financial restructuring and technological transformation, largely in response to recessionary pressures and global competition. At the same time the rate of lost-time injuries rose steadily. This article explores the relationship between these sets of factors. The meat packing industry is used as a case study of the interaction between industrial organization, the labour process, and the risk of workplace injuries. The article argues that the following factors have contributed to high and rising injury rates in the industry: consolidation into a smaller number of large, highly specialized and mechanized plants; deteriorating labour relations in the face of falling profits; and an intensified labour process stressing line speedups and a growing risk of repetitive strain injuries. These observations are supported by a detailed analysis of the relationship between the labour process and workplace injuries at one packing plant considered typical of the industry. There is no mention in particular of the proportion of this workforce that are women, and no mention of gender issues.

Pennington, S. and Westover, B. (1989). *A Hidden Workforce: Home Workers in England, 1850-1985.* **London: MacMillan Education Ltd.**

Perspective: historical, feminist, labour
Setting: British
References: 12 (chapter 1), 43 (chapter 9)
Type of article/study: descriptive, historical
Summary:

Summary: According to the authors, home work has consistently formed one of the most underpaid sectors of the capitalist economy. Problems with home work include: the evasion of minimum wage legislation, absence of occupational health and safety regulation, lack of unionisation, low pay, and, frequently, the involvement of women workers' children in the work. In the 1980s in Britain, the bulk of home work remains in the clothing industry. The authors argue that the flexibility of home work is largely a myth because the employer determines output through piece work payment, and controls work pace through the supply of materials and collection of finished work.

The book suggests that home work will continue to exist as long as there are inadequate provisions for child care. Women's confinement to the domestic sphere erodes their self-confidence and reinforces the ideology that women are primarily domestic creatures. In the 19th century, many women worked at home in order to conceal the fact that they were working from their husbands. Among immigrant workers today, who constitute a high proportion of home workers, the same reasons still apply. They may not want anyone to know that they are working so as not to diminish their personal prestige, or because their husband may not want anyone to know that they are working. Gender divisions within the clothing industry have also been by male trade unionists in attempts to hold on to their "skilled" jobs and higher wages (p. 159). Furthermore, male-based unions have not always been that sympathetic to home workers, as they saw home workers as undercutting wages and undermining collective bargaining. More recently however, the official position of trade unionists has changed, and they have encouraged home workers to join the union. However, collective action on the part of home workers is dampened by the fact that they work in isolation and at jobs requiring low skill and little imagination. Adverse health consequences are noted in this book. Citing other sources, the authors refer to commonplace ailments among home workers, including headaches, eye strain, backaches, stomach pains, depression, stress and excessive tiredness (p. 163). With the use of inflammable objects such as glue, and with the storage of goods producing crowded working conditions, fire is an obvious hazard. Even more egregious health risks have been documented such as home asbestos work (p.163). We found this book interesting because it places women's home work in historical and societal perspective. It argues that home work for women has been possible because of societal norms which dictate that women's place is in the home, because of the few options for women in the regular work force, and because of lack of affordable day care.

Quinlan, M. (1997). The implications of labour market restructuring in industrialised societies for occupational health and safety. Unpublished paper presented to the National Institute for Working Life, Stockholm. School of Industrial Relations and Organizational Behaviour, University of New South Wales, Sydney, Australia.

Perspective: industrial relations
Setting: located primarily in an Australian context, but statistics and discussion of trends in Europe, Canada, the United States and Japan.
References: 205
Type of article/study: descriptive, review.

Summary: This article summarises the recent changes in labour market structures in industrialised countries and its consequences on worker health. Changing labour market structures are often associated with forms of work organization which are more hazardous. Also, the growth of contingent work makes the measurement of the incidence of injury and disease more difficult and requires a re-thinking of regulatory strategies. Trends in industrialised societies include a significant growth in fractured, volatile and contingent forms of employment and an associated shift in forms of organization. Regional and international shifts in operations have occurred, which can undermine regulatory controls and union organization. There has been a decline in permanent full-time jobs, even in Japan. In Japan, so-called lifetime employment (which was always restricted to males in large corporations and underpinned by an extensive subcontracting system of small businesses employing women, older workers and casual labourers) has weakened over the last decade, in tandem with an increase in part-time work. An American survey found that the expansion of less secure forms of employment is not primarily a consequence of worker choice but of a combination of changed corporate employment practices and labour market conditions. The decline in full-time employment is due in part to massive lay-offs, plant closures, and out-sourcing. The pool of unemployed increases the vulnerability and reduces the bargaining power of workers in contingent forms of employment described below. Quinlan notes that the following types of work organization have increased in industrialised countries: a) Part-time work. This form of work is associated with lower levels of protection in terms of social security (health and unemployment insurance, pension and maternity entitlements) and employment regulation (leave and promotion entitlements, unfair dismissal protection). In certain sectors, for instance retailing full time workers have been replaced by part time ones. In the European Union there was a significant concentration of younger workers in temporary employment.

b) Out-sourcing, franchising and self-employment. These forms of work, particularly out-sourcing, has gained momentum in the last 15 years. Out-sourcing provides a way for firms to bypass regulatory controls and to achieve greater flexibility in labour employment practices. Out-sourcing has occurred among large private-sector firms and by the public sector. In the United Kingdom there has been a trend towards outsourcing and re-organization in the public sector (e.g. health care). The growth of the self-employment and subcontracting since the 1970s in the USA, Britain, Australia and elsewhere is at least partly the outcome of a conscious effort by employers to manipulate contractual forms in a way that evades the requirements for collective labour law (in terms of wages, leave entitlements) and other forms of regulation (for instance, workers' compensation). Self-employed workers are often sub-contracting.

c) Homework and telework. Homework is a form of outsourcing which involves both self-employed workers and employees. In the USA, the number of homeworkers fell from 4.7 million in 1960 to 2.2 million in 1980 before rising again to 3.4 million in 1990. In Britain the number of homeworkers tripled between 1981 and 1994. The typical homeworker according to the British and US surveys is a middle aged married woman with children. Homework presents major regulatory difficulties because of its invisibility to factory inspectorates and others, and due to its widespread illegal practices.

d) Agency labour. Agency, temporary help supply or labour-hire firms provide temporary workers to clients who are under the direct supervision of the client. In the United States, temporary help supply firms grew by 43% between 1989 and 1994. Over this period, there was a growing use of such firms for the supply of blue collar workers.

e) Franchising is a commercial and legal arrangement which has the capacity to evade regulatory requirements. By splintering employment units, franchising makes union organization more difficult.

f) Growth of small business and declining workplace size. Labour shedding of large organizations and the growth of outsourcing has resulted in a growth in the number and employment share of small businesses. Small businesses can be characterised by a higher rate of volatility, lower unionisation rates and lower effective regulatory coverage. Splintering workers into smaller workplaces has enabled management to use collective job insecurity to ensure cooperation. Workers in small businesses also have less job security and on-the job experience. Quinlan notes demographic differences in employment: more women are casual workers and more women are part-time. Women and older men are also less likely to be re-employed.

Roskies, E. and Louis-Guerin, C. (1990). Job insecurity in managers: Antecedents and

consequences. *Journal of Organizational Behaviour,* 11, 345-359.

Perspective: psychology, industrial relations
Setting: Three companies in Ontario and Quebec
References: 40
Type of article/study: Survey

Summary: Through a self-administered survey to 1291 managers, this study examined the reactions to job insecurity as a chronic, ambiguous threat. Many previous studies have focussed exclusively on firms in acute crisis. Although none of the managers surveyed was currently facing layoff, half worked for firms that had laid off managers in the previous five years and half worked in a stable, expanding firm. It was the individual's subjective appraisal of risk that negatively affected well-being and work effort, rather than "objective" indices of insecurity. Job insecurity encompassed much more than the fear of simply losing one's job next week or next month. The prospect of demotion, deterioration in working conditions, or the long term prospect of eventual job loss is also associated with decreased well-being and work commitment; and surprisingly, the anticipated deterioration in working conditions had the strongest impact of all. Only a minority of managers saw themselves as personally threatened and this belief in personal invulnerability held true even in companies that had laid off managers in the recent past and were likely to do so in the near future. Perception of job insecurity was related to neurotic personality traits and to objective indicators, such as working in a company at risk for downsizing or working in a department that had been downsized or re-organized in the previous two years.

Ross, R. (1990). The relative decline of relative autonomy: Global capitalism and the political economy of state change. In E.S. Greenberg and T.S. Mayer (Eds.), *Changes in the State,* **London: Sage Publications.**

Perspective: Marxist
Setting: global
References: -20
Type of article/study: descriptive

Summary: This article uses a Marxist framework to describe the nature of the shift from monopoly capitalism to global capitalism in the 1970s, 80s and 90s. In the late 19th century, monopoly capitalism had emerged out of the shell of competitive capitalism. "Restructuring", the word currently used to denote such changes, has implications for the relationship between capital and labour. As firms become global by locating parts of their production process in regions where low-wage and/or politically repressed working classes are located, labour costs decrease. The threat of further re-location provides additional leverage for management in the control of labour. At the workplace, job loss, a decline of real wages, and a loss of control over work rules, ensues. Multi-sourcing allows a firm to avoid labour difficulties at any one site. Conglomeration prevents organized labour from jeopardising the profit flow of a highly diversified corporate structure. Restructuring also has implications for capital-state relationships. During the monopoly era, the role of the state expanded. During the global era, this autonomy declines: with enhanced ability to move production to regions where state policies may be more favourable to capital, global capital is in a position to demand changes in state policy.
Schenk,C. and Anderson, J. (Eds.). (1995). *Re-shaping Work: Union Responses to Technological*

Change. **Don Mills: Ontario Federation of Labour Technological Adjustment Research Programme.**

Perspective: labour
Setting: Canada
References: numerous
Type of article/study: Collection of papers: discussion and surveys

Summary: These series of papers describe the changes in work organization and technology that are occurring at many workplaces in Canada. These include new forms of work organization such as total quality management, just in time delivery systems, lean production and agile production. The book also discusses the deregulation and decentralisation of the traditional workplaces such as home-working, sub-contracting and turning employees into self-employed workers. Papers are based on a wide array of industry sectors including garment work, building trades, steel, auto work, and postal work. The book also describes some responses to these changes in work, including government action on technology (based on some European successes), and new collective bargaining regulation.

Storper, M. and Scott, A.J. (1990). Work organization and local labour markets in an era of flexible production. *International Labour Review,* **129 (5): 573-591.**

Perspective: Marxist
Setting: USA
References: 32
Type of article/study: descriptive

Summary: The authors note that in industrialised countries from the post-world war era until the 1950s and 1960s, manufacturing processes were primarily Fordist. At the macro-level, this era was characterised by an era of social stability because of Keynesian welfare state legislation. Starting in the 1970s and 1980s, this stability was contested by increasing competition from Japan and other newly industrialising countries. Furthermore, the Fordist type of production system came up against technological and social limits to its expansion. More recently, production systems can be characterised by flexibility in both the technical aspects of production (e.g. unstandardised outputs) and in terms of the social relations of production. Labour flexibility can be achieved by: increasing the number of temporary workers, sub-contracting, using part-time workers, turn-over (e.g. temporary lay-ff and recall), and the use of home-workers. The author also notes the use of de-skilled workers, particularly in service work (p.579) and in 'back offices' (p.588). De-skilled service work is often part-time and temporary, with few fringe benefits and is supplied by such groups as suburban married women, adolescents and minorities. A San Francisco study of 'back office' workers found that they primarily employed the services of 'married women' (p.588), as employers valued their friendliness and compliance in their dealings with the public. The implications for workers include increased turn-over, fewer employees enjoying employment security, a decrease in traditional labour unions (and thus decreased wages and benefits), and rapid growth of vulnerable or dependent firms (e.g. sweat shops) in many major cities in N. America and Europe (giving rise to masses of urban poor). Furthermore, flexible markets diminish the incentive for investing in on-the-job training and the acquisition of new skills.
Tremblay, D-G. (1994). Chômage, Flexibilité et précarité d'emploi: Aspects sociaux. In F.

Dumont, S. Langlois and Y. Martin (Eds.). *Traité des Problèmes Sociaux*. Québec: Institut Québécois de Recherche sur la Culture.

Perspective: social science
Setting: Québec
References: 42
Type of article/study: descriptive
[Note: this article is in French]

Summary: The authors distinguish between four types of flexibility as the notion relates to work. These are (1) flexibility vis a vis labour costs (2) flexibility concerning when the worker works (3) flexibility concerning the employment relationship and (4) techno-organizational flexibility, which relates to the flexibility in terms of using productive equipment, technology, and may include the worker rotation of tasks within a workplace.

Tremblay notes that the growth in flexible work and insecure work has arisen in the context of four different factors: (1) the increase in service sector work and characteristics particular to this sector (2) the emergence of new forms of employment relationships (3) the increase in the unemployment rate and (4) the reduced importance of employment as a societal value in certain countries (p. 630). She suggests that countries such as Norway, Sweden, Germany and Austria accord significant importance to employment, whereas countries such as Quebec and the rest of North America do not accord very significant importance to employment levels.

Tremblay notes that it is not only employers who favour alternative forms of employment such as flexible work. Although unions are often officially opposed to 'precarious employment', enterprise-specific negotiations, in protecting the conditions of those who are already working, can sometimes encourage 'precarious employment' for the new entrants such as women and youth to work. For instance, they may accept lower wages for this group, compared to those that are unionized (and more permanent and with seniority) at the workplace. Unemployment in Quebec and Canada is higher than most other countries in the OECD (Organization of Economic Cooperation and Development). Quebec unemployment tends to hover around the 11-12% mark. Tremblay points out that employment does not appear to be an important social and collective value (compared to Norway or Sweden), in that our political and economic policies do not place a high priority on reducing the unemployment rate. This may be due to the prevailing ideology of individualism. Men and women suffer equally from unemployment, but women are somewhat protected from unemployment because of their large numbers in service, and because they are more willing to accept temporary or part-time work, compared to men. Women and young people (age 15-24 years) have a disproportionately large share of atypical employment.

Tremblay noted the following social consequences of flexible and insecure employment: lack of employment security, low wages, lack of benefits such as retirement schemes or supplementary health benefits, absence of union representatives, and reduced accessed to training and promotion. Alternative forms of employment do not appear to recede after recessions are over. Between a half to a third of workers in Quebec do not have full time permanent employment.

Some European publications suggest that societal characteristics such as laws and government programs may exert significant influence on the extent of flexible employment in various different countries. But more research is required in order to gain a better understanding of these relationships (p. 649).

Useem, M. (1994). Business restructuring and the aging workforce. In J. A. Auerbach and J. C.

Welsh (Eds.), *Aging and Competition: Rebuilding the US Workforce*, Report No.273, Washington, DC: National Planning Association.

Perspective: business
Setting: US
References: 28
Type of article/study: descriptive/discussion

Summary: In this article, restructuring is defined to include substantial company changes in ownership, financial structure, or organizational form. The authors argue that few large firms did not take any of these actions during the 1980s. The driving forces for restructuring included the recession of the early 1990s, international competition, the total quality management movement (TQM), and institutional investors. Older, uneducated, blue collar, and unionized employees bear more of the downsizing brunt as they are more likely to be in firms that have cut their workforce. At the same time, these groups enjoy more of the redesign benefits; they are over-represented in firms that increase employee involvement, introduce TQM programs and develop new work processes. The authors argue that as a result of these restructuring changes, fewer workers should be in mind-numbing or narrowly defined jobs. A study is cited that found that company executives view older workers as less flexible than younger ones. This article is useful for understanding the business perspective on restructuring.

Vahtera, J, Kivimäki, M, and Pentti, J. (1997). **Effect of organizational downsizing on health of employees. The Lancet 350: 1124-28.**

Perspective:epidemiological
Setting: Finland; 981 local government workers
References: 31
Type of article/study: prospective; before and after study

Summary: The absenteeism and ill-health of 981 local government workers (who remained in employment) was followed during a period of economic decline and downsizing from 1991 to 1995. There was a significant association between downsizing and medically certified sick leave. The rate of absenteeism was 2.3 times greater after major downsizing, classified by occupation, than after minor downsizing. There was a significant increase in musculoskeletal disorders and trauma after downsizing. Sickness absence was even greater for employees over the age of 44 years, who worked in a large workplace, who had poor health before downsizing and/or had a higher income.

Walsh, T. J. (1990). **Flexible labour utilization in the private service sector.** *Work, Employment & Society* 4 (4): 517-530.

Perspective: business
Setting: United Kingdom
References: 29
Type of article/study: descriptive, case study
Summary: Written from a pro-business stance, this paper is based on an examination of nine company

case studies. It is argued that the use of flexible labour can reduce costs to business. For instance, 'Increasing proportion of part-time, casual and temporary staff means more intensive use of labour and makes better use of capital equipment, given product demand' (p. 523). There was no discussion of health effects in the article.

Williams, S. (1996). *Our Lives Are At Stake: Women and the Fishery Crisis in Newfoundland and Labrador.* St. John's: Institute of Social and Economic Research, Memorial University.

Perspective: historical, empirical, social policy
Setting: Newfoundland and Labrador
Type of article/study: background historical research, workshops/interviews

Summary: In rural resource-dependent regions, ecological degradation is an important dimension of restructuring and its impact on women. The groundfish moratorium in 1992 affected thousands of women working in the Newfoundland and Labrador fishery. Before this closure, 15,000 women were directly employed in the industry, making up 50 percent of plant workers and 12 percent of fishers. Women worked on shore curing fish, on fish plant assembly lines, in clerical and management jobs and in the fishing boats. Nearly 10,000 women were eligible for fishery adjustment programs. Thousands of other women lost employment in businesses dependent on the fishery. Public attention has focussed on the plight of the fisherman, but women have also suffered the loss of their livelihoods. They have dealt with family and community stresses. However, women have had little say in the design of government adjustment programs or in the decisions being made about the fisher of the future. Our Lives Are at Stake combines background research with the voices of women from interviews and workshops. The report begins with a history of women in the fishery, as the women describe their work and that of their mothers and grandmothers. In the next section, women talk about coping with adjustment programs and the effect of the fishery crisis on their lives and communities. Finally, the report looks at changes in the fishery and in social policy which will affect rural communities and the work done by women. The women describe their visions of the future and their ideas for preserving rural communities.

Witherill, J.W. and Kolak, J. (1996). Is corporate re-engineering hurting your employees? *Professional Safety,* May, 28-32.

Perspective: occupational health and safety
Setting: US
References: 12
Type of article/study: descriptive/discussion, and a case study of a large firm with 2,300 employees.

Summary: The authors suggest that re-engineering or restructuring may be associated with greater lost-time accidents and with higher rates of sick time. Re-engineering can create a fearful atmosphere among employees: employees may refrain from identifying [safety] problems for fear of being perceived as negative. Furthermore, employees may take unnecessary risks in an attempt to appear productive (for instance, not adhering to time-consuming safety devices) and employees may become overwhelmed with workloads. Restructuring is often associated with poor morale, and that in turn is associated with poor productivity and increasing accidents. Though evidence for their conclusions is generally restricted to only one company, and requires confirmatory studies, their argument is plausible and is completely commensurate with the more general occupational accident literature. This article is important because it identifies links between restructuring and health which are not discussed elsewhere. The authors do not discuss any issues relating specifically to women and work.

Woodward, C., Shannon, H., Cunningham, C., McIntosh, J., Lendrum, B., Rosenbloom, D. and Brown, J. (February, 1998). Re-engineering in a large teaching hospital: A longitudinal study. McMaster University Centre for Health Economics and Policy Analysis Working Paper # 98-1. Hamilton, Ontario.

Perspective: epidemiological
Setting: Canada, health care sector
References: 43
Type of article/study: longitudinal survey design

Summary: This article describes the impact on the staff of a large teaching hospital of re-engineering and the subsequent merger of the hospital into a larger hospital corporation. A random sample of hospital employees was surveyed over a period of two years on three occasions. Most of these employees were women. The purpose was to examine changes over time in the staff's perceptions of how re-engineering affected them, their work environment and the quality of care they provide. Outcome measures included the work environment (e.g. decision latitude, job demands, social support), emotional distress, personal resources (e.g. coping, readiness for change), spillover from work to home (and vice versa), and perceptions of patient care and the hospital as an employer. The study found significant increases in depression, anxiety, emotional exhaustion and job insecurity, especially during the first year of changes. By the end of the second year, deterioration in team work, increasing lack of clarity in roles, and increasing use of 'distraction' as a coping device were evident. Job demands increased throughout the period, although there was little change in decision latitude. Overall the work environment was seen to have been negatively affected, and patient care was seen to have declined by the second year of change. By Time 3 there was a significant increase in reported interference of work with family life and vice versa. Over time there was also an increasing decline in the perceived availability of support from co-workers and supervisors. The paper discusses some of the implications of the study results, particularly the consequences of re-engineering and change in the hospital sector for employee morale, mental health, job satisfaction, levels of trust and, ultimately, for quality of care.

Canadian Data on Work Arrangements

Reports

Akyeampong, E.B. (1989). The changing face of temporary help. Perspectives on Labour and Income, Catalogue No. 75-001-XPE, Vol.1, No.2. Ottawa: Statistics Canada.

Akyeampong, EB and J Siroonian (1993). Work Arrangements of Canadians: An Overview. Perspectives on Labour and Income, Catalogue No. 75-001-XPE, Vol. 5, No. 3. Ottawa: Statistics Canada.
Akyeampong, EB (1997). Work Arrangements: 1995 Overview. Perspectives on Labour and Income,

Catalogue No. 75-001 - XPE, Vol. 9, No.1. Ottawa: Statistics Canada.

Economic Council of Canada. (1991). Employment in the Service Economy. Ottawa: Supply and Services Canada.

Krahn, (1991). Non-standard work arrangements. Perspectives on Labour and Income, Catalogue No. 75-001-XPE, Vol. 3, No.4. Ottawa: Statistics Canada.

Schellenberg, G. (1997). The Changing Nature of Part-Time Work. Social Research Series, Paper No.4. Ottawa: Canadian Council on Social Development.

Schellenberg, G . & Clark, C. (1996). Temporary Employment in Canada: Profiles, Patterns and Policy Considerations. Social Research Series, Paper No.1. Ottawa: Canadian Council on Social Development.

Data Sources of Above Reports

Labour Force Survey, Statistics Canada

Survey of Work Arrangements (1991), Statistics Canada

Survey of Work Arrangements (1995), Statistics Canada

SECTION III:
ADVOCACY TOOLS

Estrogen Through the Life Cycle

CHARLENE DAY AND MIRIAM HAWKINS, WOMEN'S HEALTHY ENVIRONMENTS NETWORK

While the hormone story a complicated one, it is more important today than ever to know about it. The last few decades have become perilous for our delicate endocrine systems in ways even many doctors may not realize. Hormone-disrupting chemicals new to our food, medicine chests and environment present a devastating threat to humans and wildlife alike. Barraged by misinformation, myths and propaganda, it's no wonder that so many of us are confused about our health and the health of our environment. But as informed citizens, we can take even greater responsibility for our health and our communities.

This commentary will focus on the hormone estrogen, whose central role in this discussion relates to its function in the body and how we may get too much, and the wrong kind, for our own good. Thousands of widely-used drugs and chemicals are estrogenic in nature or effect. They are hormone disruptive, and may seriously affect our health and, even more, that of our offspring. They are linked with dramatic increases in such effects as infertility, genital deformities, hormonally triggered cancers like those of the breast and prostrate gland, low sperm counts, hyperactivity and other neurological disorders. It should be noted that "man-made chemicals scramble all sorts of hormone messages", hitting the adrenal and thyroid glands hardest, according to Linda Birnbaum of the U.S. Environmental Protection Agency. Depressed thyroid levels have been linked to breast cancer just as increased estrogen has (19).

The extent of lifelong exposure to estrogen (especially synthetic forms) is a major health risk factor. In some ways, there are choices, like safe, effective and natural ways of balancing estrogen in the body. Hormone disrupting chemicals in the environment are a more difficult story. It is hoped that you will be able to use this information to ask serious questions of health providers, industry and government and to investigate safe alternative approaches.

Types of Estogen

There are four types of estrogens: those naturally occurring in the body, those synthesized for ingestion as medications, "xeno" or foreign estrogens from modern industrial and household chemicals, and phytoestrogens from food plants, many of which provide important health benefits.

Natural Estrogen

Some 50 known hormone molecules carry instructions from more than a dozen endocrine glands and tissues to cells all over the body to control many bodily functions, including reproduction, sexual development, growth, maintenance of metabolism and response to external stimuli.

Natural estrogens are a group of several fat-soluble steroid hormones made primarily in the female ovaries and the male testes (but also throughout the body) in humans and other vertebrates from cholesterol or acetyl coenzyme-A. Known as the female hormones (in whom they're more plentiful), they not only bring out feminine traits and control reproductive cycles but also more generally influence growth, development and behaviour, immunity, skin, bone, the cardiovascular system, liver, and even the brain, ensuring the balance of normal body systems. Estrogens stimulate tissue growth by promoting cell proliferation in female sex organs (breasts, uterus), increasing a cell's size (as in female breast and male muscle during puberty), and by making specific proteins. In males, estrogens play a secondary role to androgens, mainly the hormone testosterone, which defines male characteristics (too much estrogen can feminize these). Lifetime exposure to natural estrogens also varies according to diet and exercise. Since the body stores estrogen in (especially abdominal) fat, obesity increases exposure.

Only three estrogens are naturally present in significant quantities: estradiol, estrone, and estriol. Estradiol is the most abundant and potent estrogen hormone, 12 times stronger than estrone and 80 times stronger than estriol, an estrone derivative. There are "good" and "bad" forms of estrogen (the "bad" can trigger cancer)(5). The body tries to maintain optimal levels in the blood with a hypothalamus and pituitary response to low levels, triggering female ovaries to secrete estradiol and progesterone and male testes to secrete testosterone (excess becomes estrogen) until a certain blood level is reached. This feedback loop is influenced by the liver, which degrades some unneeded natural hormones from the system within hours.

Before birth, both placental and fetal hormones act upon the developing baby. For males, after the chromosomal determination of sex at about seven weeks, masculinization depends on correct relaying of hormonal cues from the testicles. In females, ovaries develop at three to four months which will synthesize estrogen. But very tiny amounts of foreign estrogenic substances at critical prenatal stages can interfere with sexual, reproductive, behavioural and neurological development. In *Our Stolen Future*, authors Theo Colborn et al. note,

> At the same time as hormones are guiding at least some aspects of sexual development, they are orchestrating the growth of the baby's nervous and immune systems, and programming organs and tissues such as the liver, blood, kidneys and muscles, which function differently in men and women.... For all these systems, normal development depends on getting the right hormone messages in the right amount to the right place at the right time.... If something disrupts the cues during a critical period of development, it can have very serious consequences for the offspring.

Estrogen and compounds that trick estrogen receptors are particularly key at this stage, during the first few years of life and again at puberty when critical cell division takes place.

In females, puberty, the menstrual cycle, pregnancy and menopause are important estrogen-related events. Around age ten, the hypothalamus stimulates the ovaries to produce estrogen and progesterone, which prompt physical changes such as budding of the breasts, growth of pubic hair, increasing height and weight, and skin changes. Usually at about age 12, menstruation begins. Hormones are released at dramatically different rates during the 28-day menstrual cycle. For the first 8 to 11 days, the ovaries make lots of estrogen, falling off about day 13, when progesterone begins to rise and ovulation occurs (progesterone causing ovulatory libido). After 10 or 12 days, if fertilization does not occur, ovarian progesterone falls dramatically, triggering menses and a renewal of the cycle. If it does occur, an estrogen spike precedes a progesterone-rich gestation which maintains pregnancy and permanently matures breast cells (to divide more slowly). For several months after birth, breast fluid is low in estrogen. Before age 30, pregnancy appears to protect breast cells from abnormal changes that excess estrogen and hormone disruptors may cause. Progesterone opposes the growth-stimulating action of estrogen in the body.

Between 40 and 50 years of age, the interaction between hormones changes, leading to menopause.

As fewer egg follicles are stimulated, the amount of estrogen and progesterone produced by the ovaries declines, menstruation becomes scantier and erratic and eventually ceases. However, other body sites such as the adrenal glands, skin, muscle, brain, pineal gland, hair follicles and body fat are capable of making our hormones, enabling the female body to make healthy adjustments in hormonal balance after menopause. This is provided a woman has taken good care of herself during the premenopausal years with sensible lifestyle, diet, and attention to mental and emotional health. Among other factors, obesity and sedentary lifestyles promote early onset of puberty and late menopause, increasing overall as well as "bad" estrogen exposure and related risks.

Synthetic Estrogen

Synthetic estrogens, found in pharmaceutical products, "… have had their molecular structure altered so they can be patented. They tend to be more potent than the body's own estrogens and more toxic" (12).

The Pill

Today, millions of women take hormone contraceptives (oral, implanted or injectable). Made with different amounts and potencies of synthetic estrogens, progestins, or both, which the body does not easily break down, they primarily work by maintaining high levels of estrogen in the body to prevent ovulation. Suppressing natural hormones with synthetic ones literally stops menses. Bleeding occurs each month only because the synthetic hormones are not taken for seven days of the cycle and would be more accurately termed "withdrawal bleeding," not menstruation. No scientific proof validates that the Pill is safe. According to Nancy Beckham in *Menopause—A Positive Approach Using Natural Therapies,* "Women on the Pill have a greater tendency to liver dysfunction and to more allergies. Vitamin A levels may be raised in the blood; vitamins B12 and C … lowered."

Although initial trials were flawed, the first generation Pill was widely marketed as an effective, safe and convenient method of birth control, a shock to such early researchers as Dr. Ellen Grant, author of *The Bitter Pill and Sexual Chemistry,* who felt synthetic hormones should have been withdrawn from the market due to their known serious side effects. According to Dr. Samuel Epstein in *The Breast Cancer Prevention Program,* dozens of studies confirm side effects such as risk of heart attack and stroke, diabetes, gallbladder disease, liver cancer and, exposing breast tissue to excess estrogen, up to ten times greater risk of breast cancer, especially with early or prolonged use (8).

Changes since the early 1960s were supposed to make the second generation Pill (ethinyl estradiol) safer, but it actually binds with estrogen receptors in the breast and is 40 times more potent than estradiol. The combined Pill also increases the risk of coronary artery disease, breast cancer and high blood pressure. The side effects include nausea, vomiting, headaches, breast tenderness, weight increases, changes in sex drive, depression, blood clots and increased incidence of vaginitis. Also, women with a history of epilepsy, migraine, asthma or heart disease may find their symptoms worsen. Many of these effects may persist long after women discontinue taking the Pill. Furthermore, smoking while taking the Pill accentuates these risks. A third generation progestin-only implant "Pill" is also problematic, as hundreds of lawsuits against Norplant's maker attest, while an injectable progestin Depo-Provera increases breast cancer risk in many studies (8).

Estrogen (Hormone) Replacement Therapy – HRT

Perhaps there's no topic of greater confusion to women than hormone replacement therapy, the next big hormone drug promotion after the Pill. The menopausal woman has become another lucrative market for synthetic hormones, now available in pills, patches and implants. One of the most popular is Premarin, made from the urine of pregnant mares.

Proclaimed as the primary missing ingredient for the menopausal woman, estrogen is also strongly recommended by modern medicine for the prevention of cardiovascular disease and osteoporosis. Most doctors today warn women of the risks of going through menopause and, for that matter, the post-menopausal years, without the protection of estrogen. Other opinions may not be offered. Because HRT is given at lower doses than the Pill, the side effects are often more subtle and slower to show up.

Women must think very carefully about the HRT decision. While most doctors are sincerely concerned about their patients, much of their education and product information comes directly from the pharmaceutical companies. Since most women also lack essential awareness about their options, decisions about menopause can be difficult. In *What Your Doctor May Not Tell You About Menopause*, Dr. John Lee has compiled a list of side effects that can result from taking HRT. They include: increased risk of endometrial cancer, increased body fat, salt and fluid retention, depression and headaches, impaired blood sugar control (hypoglycemia), loss of zinc and retention of copper, reduced oxygen levels in all cells, thickened bile and promoted gall bladder disease, increased likelihood of breast fibrocysts and uterine fibroids, interference with thyroid activity, decreased sex drive, excessive blood-clotting, reduced vascular tone, endometriosis, uterine cramping, infertility, and restraint of osteoclast function (necessary for the health and repair of bone). According to Dr. Epstein, HRT also promotes breast, liver and ovarian cancers, weight gain and other symptoms. He recommends non-hormonal solutions: if you do use HRT, take low does over short term only, with avoidance of alcohol and smoking (12).

The intense estrogen-forming effect of alcohol can be dangerous, especially for women on HRT (see "Ways to Reduce..." #4 for more on alcohol and estrogen). Various studies show alcohol to increase breast cancer risk: even one half drink of wine may double blood estrogen for women on HRT and phenomenally increases risk for breast cancer (8).

Other Drugs

Other drugs may also be hormonally active: Tamoxifen, for example, and related raloxifene, are synthetic hormonal drugs being promoted for prevention of breast cancer, but trials reflect serious risks from both estrogenic and antiestrogenic effects. Various antihypertensives, cholesterol-lowering drugs, antibiotics, antacids, psychotherapeutics, cancer drugs and marijuana may also be of concern (8).

"Xenoestrogens" (Pseudoestrogens)

The name "xenoestrogens" is loosely applied to a host of toxic manmade chemicals which confuse estrogen receptor sites in the body and interfere with natural biochemical messages. These may be estrogen-like compounds or have an ability to mimic and or block natural hormones. They can also alter how natural hormones and their protein receptors are made, broken down and perform. Mounting research reveals an alarming situation worldwide created by the inundation of these hormone disruptors.

Because they degrade so slowly, disperse globally in air and water currents, and build up in living tissues, such persistent toxic chemicals now contaminate every ecosystem and organism on earth – and will for decades to come. Not easily excreted, they are fat-soluble, accumulating in fat, tissue, the brain, and in sex and other organs. Amounts of these toxins biomagnify up the food chain, with worst concentrations in animal- or insect-eating animals like many humans and other mammals, birds and reptiles. In one type of fish-eating Great Lakes gulls, for example, the familiar xenoestrogenic PCBs reach concentrations up to 25 million times those found in sediments, with serious results (3).

Distributing the principle functions of estrogens and androgens may unleash a torrent of reproductive and developmental health challenges, evidenced by studies of laboratory animals, cell cultures, wildlife and humans. Theo Colborn *et al* identify 51 families of synthetic chemicals that disrupt the endocrine system, including 209 PCBs, 75 dioxins and 135 furans. They are linked not only to the discovery that human sperm counts have plunged by 50 per cent globally between 1938 and 1990, but also to altered sexual behaviour, lowered immunity, and genital deformities, breast, ovarian, uterine, prostate and testicular cancer, and neurological disorders. Fibrocystic disease of the breast, polycystic ovarian syndrome, endometriosis, uterine fibroids and pelvic inflammatory diseases are also suspected. Problems may be influenced by developmental or chronic lifetime exposures (3).

The potential consequences of this overexposure are staggering, especially for our offspring. Fetuses and embryos, whose growth and development are highly controlled by the endocrine system, receive contaminants prenatally in eggs (amphibians, reptiles, birds) or the womb (mammals). Although exposed adults may not show any ill effects, their offspring may have lifelong permanent health and reproductive abnormalities. In addition to those cited above, effects include masculinization of females, feminization of males (reduced testes and penis size), undescended testicles and altered bone density and structure (3). Neonatal exposure, such as breastfeeding newborns, further concentrates body burdens.

Xenoestrogens are mostly from the petrochemical industry and, unfortunately for our health, petrochemicals are now everywhere. Machines, cars, even some power plants, run on such petrochemicals as gasoline, diesel, natural gas and the like. Many hormone disruptors are organochlorines, produced by reacting chlorine gas with petroleum hydrocarbons. They're used in plastics, pesticides, solvents, dry cleaning agents, refrigerants and other chemicals. Thousands more are by-products of the disinfection of water, bleaching of paper and incineration of chlorinated products. Millions of products, including various plastics (polyvinyl chlorides or PVCs and polycarbonated plastics found in babies' bottles, toys, food containers, and water jugs), PCBs, medicines, clothing, foods, household cleaners, air deodorizers, personal care products (cosmetics, perfumes, antiperspirants, soaps, toothpaste and mouthwash), pesticides and herbicides (DDT, dieldrin, heptachlor, etc.) either contain or are made from petrochemicals. Many of us work and live in highly toxic areas where synergistic effects can render "safe" doses of different chemicals, medicines, radiation, electromagnetic frequencies etc. hundreds of times more toxic when together.

Sixteen persistent toxic chemicals (known as "POPs" – persistent organic pollutants) have been targeted for priority action by the United Nations. Although Canada banned many of these (DDT, PCBs and others known to cause birth defects, reproductive failure and near-extinction of a wide range of species) decades ago, they continue to be manufactured and used worldwide. At least six – PCBs, dioxins, furans, hexachlorobenzene (HCB), lindane and short-chain chlorinated paraffins – are still generated, produced and/or used in Canada. Drinking water may be contaminated by other proven estrogenic compounds nonylphenol (NP) and endosulfan, still being used in plastics and pesticides manufacturing as well as in liquid laundry detergent, all-purpose cleaners, soaps and shampoos. Hormone-disrupting compounds like phthalates are used as plasticizers in PVC as well as paints, inks and glues. Waste plastics may be the most important source of high amounts and frequencies of toxic PVC stabilizer bisphenol-A in landfill leachate (Chemosphere, March 1999). It's vastly worse when burned.

Airborne ash from industry, garbage or hazardous waste incinerators is often high in hormone disruptors and carcinogens like dioxin (one of the most virulent) as well as lead, mercury and cadmium, the original hormone disruptors. This ash lands on plants eaten by us as well as livestock and fish, which pass concentrated toxins on to humans. House dust, old paint and stagnant tap water are other common sources of lead. As well as petrochemicals, burning fossil fuels releases cadmium and mercury. Mercury can also be a serious dental hazard. Two percent of people in cities over one million people have ten times the mercury blood level threshold for neurological effects (6).

Our food is one of the most unwitting pathways for hormone disrupting chemicals. Processed foods, whose often excess sugar and hydrogenated fats weaken immunity, now comprise 80% of our food supply. Packaging, preservatives, artificial colour and flavourings may all be hazardous. For example, Red Dye No. 3, a powerful carcinogen, is still widely used. Plastic containers, styrene cups, food packaging or can liners may contain PVCs, alkylphenols, nonylphenols, bisphenol-A and phthalates, known xenoestrogens which migrate into food when heated or stored for long periods. One such is DEHA, found in some commercial cling wraps. Industry and U.S. government studies have linked DEHA to development effects in animals, but levels in some U.S. plastic wrapped cheese have been found to exceed government limits by a factor of 300,000 times. DEHA may also be contaminating other wrapped foods – especially high fat content foods such as meats. Plastic hardener bisphenol-A, found in polycarbonate baby bottles, was identified by a 1997 U.S. government report as an endocrine-disrupting chemical that consistently leached from polycarbonate into liquid when heated (peer-reviewed scientific studies found biological effects at extremely low levels). A 1999 Consumer's Union study replicated FDA's findings and advised parents to switch to baby bottles made from something other than polycarbonate plastic, as 12 groups petition the FDA and plastics manufacturers to eliminate or greatly reduced children's exposure to it (8) (see "Ways", #7a).

Produce is risky, too: an average 25% (often more) of all regular produce both grown in Canada and imported show residues of pesticides, says the 1999 report of Canada's new Commissioner of the Environment and Sustainable Development. Many are or contain hormone disruptors. World Wildlife Fund Canada (WWFC) has called on Health Minister Allan Rock to act on about two dozen pesticides considered to be endocrine disruptors. Most are registered for use on food crops and some for use inside homes, schools and daycares. Numerous areas are severely contaminated by agriculture, golf courses and cosmetic uses in Canada.

Food animals are a major source of hormonally active chemicals in our food and waterways. Animal and dairy fat has high concentrations – beef and diary products are the worst, with high residues of DDT and other chlorinated pesticides, antibiotics, veterinary drugs and growth-stimulating sex hormones. Hormone ear implants used in virtually all feedlot beef are largely unregulated. Residues up to 300 times legal limits often found in meat are from implants commonly but illegally put in muscle for faster results. Growth hormone rBGH in milk cattle produces high levels of Insulin-like Growth Factor, which encourages cell division and breast cancer malignancies but is not labeled on US products containing it (8) (labeling was outlawed by regulators in concert with rBGH producer Monsanto. Citizens' action has led to a temporary ban in Canada). Pesticides accumulate in animal fat: 15 pounds of grain produce one pound of beef, concentrating pesticides. Nitrites in ham and bacon become potent cancer causing nitrosamines in the body. Fish from industrialized waterways are contaminated with a wide range of pseudoestrogens. For example, all Great Lakes salmon show enlarged thyroid glands in recent years (6).

Taking it one step further, synthetic estrogens are also being dumped into the waterways through the urine of women and enter our food chain. This has also increased our levels of environmental estrogen exposure.

Reversing Estrogen Dominance

Dr. John Lee finds that many women are suffering from the effects of too much estrogen or "estrogen dominance." He notes that stress, nutritional deficiencies, xenoestrogens, and synthetic estrogens cause an imbalance between estrogen and progesterone. This estrogen dominance means that estrogen has begun to overshadow the other players, creating biochemical dissonance. Obviously, one key solution is to reduce excess estrogen at the sources, whether they be synthetic drugs or xenoestrogens. Eating to protect hormone balance is another key, discussed below. However, Dr. Lee has also been able to help women to balance the estrogen-dominance effect through the use of transdermal natural progesterone cream, which can correct the likely problem: progesterone deficiency. This helps to alleviate such prevalent menopausal symptoms as hot flashes and vaginal dryness. Natural progesterone, a cholesterol derivative, is made from wild Mexican yams or soybeans whose active ingredients are an exact molecular match of the body's own progesterone. It is not known to have any side effects, is non-patentable and inexpensive (use the cream under supervision of a qualified health provider. Call the company to ensure it does contain progesterone—some brands do not).

It is interesting to note that in South America and Asia where women eat wild yams or soybeans, the term "hot flash" doesn't exist in the languages, while half of all menopausal women in the North America complain of the problem. Japanese women have half the rate of hip fractures from osteoporos than North American women (they also eat less protein and do more physical, weight-bearing work) and preliminary studies suggest that soy may help retain bone mass. Dr. Lee believes that the use of natural progesterone in conjunction with dietary and lifestyle change can not only stop osteoporosis, but can actually reverse it, even in women aged 70 or more (11,12).

Eating right may really be one of our best lines of defense.

Safe Alternatives – Phytoestrogens

Plant estrogens, called phytoestrogens, are natural compounds found in hundred of food plants including herbs and seasonings which can act like natural estrogens in the body with the help of intestinal bacteria, enzymes, vitamins and minerals. Some 20 phytoestrogens have been identified in such plants as wheat, oats, rye, barley, rice and soybeans; apples, cherries, plums and pomegranates; potatoes, carrots, peas, beans; parsley, sage, garlic and coffee. Effects vary widely depending on age, sex and other factors. Fetuses and babies can even be negatively sensitive to excess plant estrogens. Adults may help reduce health risks from synthetic and xenoestrogens by lowering lifetime estrogenic exposures: phytoestrogens compete for estrogen receptor sites or positively influence estrogen metabolism. Like natural hormones, phytoestrogens are easily broken down by our bodies and spend very little time in our system (3).

Normal dietary use of phytoestrogens seems to protect against breast and reproductive cancers in humans and can be used as treatments for menopause and osteoporosis. They act as weak estrogens and appear to produce estrogen effects in postmenopausal women and anti-estrogen effects in premenopausal women. Phytoestrogens thus have this ability to act as "balancers" – raising low levels and lowering high levels of estrogen and replacing a strong estrogen with a weaker one. Effects on prenatal and neonatal development are less clear, and suggest caution with respect to soy infant formulas, for example, as well as certain nutritional supplements, herbs and even some foods during pregnancy (3).

Soy isoflavones are one of the best studied sources of phytoestrogens. One form, genistein, has been shown to have cytostatic activity against human mammory cancer cell lines in vitro and to suppress mammary tumours in rats in recent studies. Soybean products in the Asian diet may account for the low incidence of breast cancer there. A 1992 study showed Japanese women on a low-fat, soybean rich diet had up to 1,000 times more phytoestrogens in their urine than American and Finnish women. Soybeans are also a high-quality protein, a source of omega-3 fatty acids, calcium and antioxidants that protect cells from damage caused by cancer-causing free radicals. Soy peptides can boost the immune system, helping the body to fight disease. Numerous studies reveal that people who eat soy foods are at lower risk of developing breast, colon, lung and prostate cancer than those who do not. Other studies attest to soy's cholesterol-lowering properties, especially for people with high levels. Soy protein is easier on the kidneys than animal protein and may slow down or prevent kidney damage in people with impaired kidney function. Be sure to buy only organic soybeans as most others are genetically engineered or have been sprayed. Please note that soy sauce and processed soy cheeses, hot dogs, bacon and oil may not be good sources, depending on the processing.

Conclusion

Every woman should read, question, trust her natural instincts and learn about her own body. It is also essential that a woman honour her own cyclic nature and intuitive wisdom. It is a woman's right to choose with dignity the best approach to her own health care. Certainly, women have it well within their own power and knowledge to find safe, natural and effective ways to heal themselves. Healing the world, however, requires effective strategies and actions by people, governments and industry. Here are a number of ways that you can do both.

Ways to Reduce Hormone Disruption

1. Make educated decisions about the use of drugs, especially synthetic estrogens in birth control pills and hormone replacement therapy. Alternatives to HRT can be found in *Menopause & Homeopathy* by Ifeoma Ikenze, MD as well as in Susan Weed's book (20). Consult the *Physician's Desk Reference* or check the *Breast Cancer Prevention Program* (8) for known and undisclosed dangers of drugs.

2. Ask politicians and industry to take action to reduce hormone-disrupting chemicals in our environment and to evaluate chemicals and drugs for their synergistic effect before approval. Support campaigns to push Ottawa to negotiate and sign a legally-binding treaty to phase out persistent toxic chemicals worldwide and strengthen the Canadian Environmental Protection Act and Pest Control Products Act (amendments to the new CEPA include a world-first precautionary definition of "endocrine disruptor" but no Ministerial action). Canada should ban the import of products containing or manufactured with these chemicals, withdraw subsidies for activities that generate them and report annually on all uses, sources and stockpiles. We should carefully destroy all PCBs and phase out activities that generate dioxins and furans—top sources include municipal waste and sludge incineration, chlorine bleaching of paper, and improper incineration of toxic waste.

3. Do not smoke or stay in "smoky" environments—tobacco smoke contains a multitude of carcinogens.

4. Assess the risks and benefits of drinking alcohol carefully. Boosting estrogen levels, moderate drinking may offer limited protection at times. But negative effects include impaired mela-tonin secretion (a cancer suppressant) and promotion of liver enzymes that raise "bad" estrogen levels. The 1995 Nurse's Health study showed three drinks increase breast cancer risk for all women by more than 200 percent. It also inactivates immune cells, which may explain why heavy drinkers have double or higher rates of breast, liver and digestive system cancer. Binge drinking (several at one sitting) can trigger the spread of tumour cells by suppressing the body's killer cells (8).

5. Try to drink only purified water – a reverse osmosis filter on your water system is ideal, a charcoal filter removes lead.

6. Choose your food intelligently:

•Avoid processed foods and read product labels. Fruits, vegetables and whole grains, nuts, seeds and legumes offer many protective benefits.
•Buy or grow organic fruits and vegetables as much as possible: beware of perfect-looking (sprayed!) produce.
•Always wash fruits and vegetables well with a non-toxic cleanser and remove outer leaves of leafy vegetables.
•Avoid animal and dairy fat as much as possible to reduce your lifetime accumulation of POPs. Purchase hormone-free meat. Turkey is one of the safest (8).
•Beware of fish from industrialized waterways, paying attention to government warnings, especially with fatty salmon and trout. Seafood is safer (6,8).
•Consume diets rich in soy products, cabbage, broccoli, Brussels sprouts and cauliflower.
•Avoid heat-pressed oils, margarine and fried foods, opting for olive oil and organic butter.
•Investigate vitamin, mineral and amino acid supplementation as well as probiotics (digestive bacteria).
•Detoxify your liver on a regular basis using natural herbal substances. See books such as Susun Weed's (20) to safeguard the liver's removal of estrogens from the blood.

7. Since "it is simply not known which plastics contain hormone-disrupting chemicals, and because the manufacture and disposal of some plastics can release such pollutants, precautions should probably be taken with all plastics," the WWFC warns. Lobby for safe products like nonplasticized plastic packaging materials and polymerized plasticizers in cling wrap, which reduce migration dramatically. Baby bottles can be made from plastics without bisphenol-A!

a) Avoid plastic containers, styrene cups, food packaging or liners that may contain pseudoestrogens which migrate into food when heated or stored for long periods. Store and microwave food in glass containers. You can order glass baby bottles and freeze food in unsealed glass (leave two inches room to expand at the top, seal later). Avoid plastic cling wrap (minimizing food contact) and fatty foods in plastic heat-seal (freezer wrap is better). Read labels and call 1-800 numbers for information on product formulations.
b) Avoid plastics made from PVC, labeled #3 on such products as: packaging for personal care and household cleaning products, venetian blinds, shower curtains, office, auto and building supplies. Of particular concern are items that children contact—such as toys, vinyl flooring and furniture. Stick to wood or natural fibres. Hospital and health care products are a prime source both for IV patients and the community: when incinerated, PVC plastic can create dioxins and furans. Join with your local Health Care Without Harm activist group (like TEA) to lobby hospitals to replace IV bags and tubes with those not containing PVCs and to stop incineration of such medical waste (22).

8. Make moderate exercise a regular part of your life: exercise results in less exposure to natural estrogens, late menarche, fewer periods and early menopause, increase "good" estrogen and estrogen-binding proteins, reducing breast cancer risk by diverting estrogen away from sensitive

breast cells. Try to de-stress your life and get plenty of sleep and meditate. This also helps your adrenal glands (8).

9. Personal care products are a minefield of hazards. Alkaline cleansers (most supermarket soaps) destroy skin's "acid mantle", your first line of defense against chemicals. Avoid all such products containing petrochemicals (including cosmetics, sun screens and mosquito repellents). Avoid spermicides and vaginal gels that contain nonylphenols. Replace permanent and semi-permanent hair dyes with henna, herbal or safe products – typical (especially dark) hair dyes contain a wide range of carcinogenic ingredients and toxic contaminants that rapidly absorb through the scalp. Studies have linked some to breast cancer, non-Hodgkin's lymphoma and multiple myeloma (8).

10. Avoid pesticides and home-pest strips. Use natural lawn and garden maintenance methods (call TEA for tips). If you golf, keep hands, tees and golf balls away from your mouth (most golf courses are intensively sprayed). Canada should de-register all pesticides containing hexachlorobenzene, dioxins and/or furans or other persistent toxic chemicals. 2,4-D based weed killers may contain dioxins and HCB. Manufacturers should be required to disprove hormone disrupting potential. Uses which expose children should be de-registered. NPEs (see #11) may be present in the pesticide formulation but not indicated on the label (see below). Avoid lindane and synthetic pyrethroid-based head lice and scabies shampoo for humans and flea shampoo for pets (lindane should be banned and is being withdrawn by canola growers who use it on seeds) (22). Apply olive oil and then vinegar and rinse or contact LiceBusters at (416) 410-LICE.

11. Nonylphenol ethoxylates (NPEs) break down into hormone disrupting nonylphenols in sludge and waterways. NPEs are used in liquid laundry detergent, all-purpose cleaners, soaps and shampoos as well as in pesticides, oil and gas extraction, pulp and paper and textiles. Avoid "super-strength" cleaners—NPEs are likely used. Select soaps and detergents, especially liquid, which the manufacturer assures you do not contain NPEs. Use non-toxic cleaning products like baking soda, borax and vinegar or green products, avoiding chlorine and phosphates. Minimize car and energy use. NPEs are used in oil and gas drilling, extraction and production. Encourage worldwide listing of nonylphenols by chemical manufacturers on products sold to consumers (22).

12. Question nuclear safety: radiation from nuclear power plants and typical mammography machines can damage cellular DNA and affect hormones. Promote energy efficiency and safe power production (take part right away in the plutonium importation consultation on the Government of Canada website). Lobby for thermography and safe diagnostics, and practice breast self-exam (8).

13. Electromagnetic fields may disrupt normal body electrical systems and immunity. Choose low EMF appliances and keep at a safe distance— at least two feet for most small units and more for microwaves. Cell phones and towers can emit harmful levels of microwaves. EMFs as well as light at night, inhibit melatonin (8).

14. Avoid spray paints, strippers and aerosols. Choose lead-free paint. Wash hands, floors and windowsills often (22).

15. Treat dead batteries as hazardous waste. Avoid mercury amalgam dental fillings. Ask about porcelain, gold or composite fillings for new or replacement fillings (22).

16. Avoid chlorine as much as possible. Promote ozone rather than chlorine for swimming pools. Choose paper products bleached without chlorine processes, which create dioxins and furans, two of the most dangerous POPs.

17. Don't reuse old utility poles and railway ties for garden and construction projects since most poles and some ties were treated with pentachlorophenol (PCP) and leach dioxins, furans and hexachlorobenzene (HCB) (22).

18. Insist on a safe workplace.

19. Become involved at the grassroots level by joining a group such as Women's Network on Health and the Environment. Show WNH&E's film *Exposure: Environmental Links to Breast Cancer* and read the resource guide, *Taking Action for a Healthy Future*, for many more references as well as those cited below.

20. Consult websites and publications of the World Wildlife Fund (www.wwfcanada.org) and Center for Bioenvironmental Research at Tulane and Xavier Universities (http://e.hormone.tulane.edu/), which also tracks international news and research.

21. Follow up: "Environmental Hormones: Past, Present, Future". A Symposium Marking the 20th Anniversary of the First Meeting on Estrogens in the Environment (1979-1999) Oct. 18-20/99, Tulane University, New Orleans, Louisiana; e.hormone@tulane.edu.

Permission for the reprinting of this paper was received by Dorothy Goldin Rosenberg of the Women's Health & Environments Network as this was first published in "Connections Extra: Women's Health & Environments Network" Issue 14 – extra, Fall 1999.

References

Ahlgrimm, Marla and Kells, John. *The HRT Solution, Optimizing Your Hormone Potential.* N.Y.: Avery Publishing Group, 1999.

Austin, Steve and Hitchcock, Cathy. *Breast Cancer, What you should know (but may not be told) about Prevention, Diagnosis and Treatment.* Rocklin, CA: Prima Publishing. 1994.

Colborn, Theo, Dianne Dumanoski and John Peterson Meyers. *Our Stolen Future: Are We Threatening Our Fertility, Intelligence and Survival?* NY: Penguin Books, 1997.

Coney, Sandra. *The Menopause Industry, How the medical establishment exploits women.* Alameda, CA: Hunter House Publishing, 1994.

Davis, Devra Lee, and Bradlow, H. Leon. Can Environmental Estrogens Cause Breast Cancer? *Scientific American.* October 1995, p. 166.

DeRosa, Christopher, et al. Environmental Exposures that Affect the Endocrine System: Public Health Implications. *Journal of Toxicology and Environmental Health, Part B.* 1:3-26, 1998.

Diamond, Harvey. *You Can Prevent Breast Cancer.* San Diego: ProMotion Publishing, 1995.

Epstein, Samuel, M.D. and Steinman, David. *The Breast Cancer Prevention Program*. N.Y.: Simon & Schuster Macmillan Co. 1997.

Fisher, William L. *How to Fight Cancer & Win*. Vancouver: Alive Books, 1988.

Guyton, Arthur, M.D. *Textbook of Medical Physiology*. PA. W. B. Saunders Co. 1981.

Lee, John, M.D. *Natural Progesterone*. Sebastopol, CA: BLL Publishing. 1994.

Lee, John, M.D. *What Your Doctor may not tell you About Menopause*. N.Y.: Warner Books. 1996.

Liew, Lana, M.D. *The Natural Estrogen Diet*. CA: Hunter House. 1999.

Love, Susan, M.D. *Dr. Susan Love's Hormone Book, Making Informed Choices About Menopause*. N.Y.: Random House, Inc. 1998.

Moss, Ralph W. *Cancer Therapy, The Independent Consumer's Guide to Non-Toxic Treatment & Prevention*. N.Y.: Random House, Inc. 1993.

Moss, Ralph W. *The Cancer Industry*. New York: Paragon House, Inc. 1991.

Northrup, Christiane, M.D. *Women's Bodies, Women's Wisdom, Creating Physical and Emotional Health and Healing*. N.Y.: Bantam Books. 1998.

Roberts, Wayne; MacRae, Rod; Stahlbrand, Lori. *Real Food For a Change. How the Simple Act of Eating Can: Boost Your Energy, Knock Out Stress, Revive Your Community, Clean Up the Planet*. Toronto: Random House. 1999.

Shandler, Nina. *Estrogen: The Natural Way*. N.Y.: Villard Books. 1997.

Tulane and Xavier Universities Center for Bioenvironmental Research (http://e.hormone.tulane.edu).

Weed, Susun. *Menopausal Years: The Wise Women Way. Alternative Approaches for Women 30-90*. Woodstock, N.Y.: Ashtree Publishing. 1992.

Weiss, Rick. 1994. Estrogen in the environment. *The Washington Post*, January 25: 10-13.

World Wildlife Fund Canada: www.wwfcanada.org; *Reducing Your Risk. A Guide to Avoiding Hormone Disrupting Chemicals; Reducing Your Risk From Pesticides*.

Wright, Jonathan, M.D. and Morgenthaler, John. *Natural Hormone Replacement*. CA: Smart Publications. 1997.

A Different Prescription

Considerations for Women's Health Groups Contemplating Funding from the Pharmaceutical Industry

ANNE ROCHON FORD, WORKING GROUP ON WOMEN AND HEALTH PROTECTION

In May of 1997, a number of Toronto-based women's organizations (the National Network on Environments and Women's Health, the Institute for Feminist Legal Studies at York, DES Action and the Toronto Women's Health Network) sponsored a panel discussion entitled: "Ethical Issues in Women's Health: The Delicate Business of Funding from Drug Companies". To this event, we invited four panellists to discuss their perspective on the issue of accepting money from the pharmaceutical industry. New insights were gained from that panel discussion. This booklet is meant to reflect some of the ideas that were presented that evening in the hope that it may help other organizations making decisions about this issue.

To do that, we have taken a scenario which represents a composite of most of the issues presented at that panel discussion and have broken down the different opinions on it. Most of the text reflects discussions which ensued from the panellists presentations.

Introduction

In Canada over the past ten years, community-based women's health organizations have been experiencing continued cutbacks from the governments which have traditionally funded them. Although no organizations were given lavish budgets, they nonetheless counted on renewal of public money to carry out the work they did in providing services and information to women about their health.

At the same time, non-profit organizations in many sectors – not just health – are being strongly encouraged to form "partnerships" with industry. Although it is not always clear exactly what is meant by "partnerships", one thing that is usually implied is the assumption that money should be sought from industry and if money is offered it should not be refused. It is easy to understand why government funders are so anxious to see non-profit organizations turn to the private sector for money. They would like to find ways to reduce their deficit and, in the case of the pharmaceutical industry, they have a vested interest in the promotion of their products which may be used by these organizations. The private sector is also being urged by government to form such partnerships and there is a constant pressure on the industry to be good corporate citizens. It is in their best corporate interest to spread the wealth and to give generously to community-based organizations and enter into sponsorship arrangements with them.

Sounds pretty straightforward. But is it? Opinions vary greatly on this topic. If you are reading this, you may be just such an organization which is struggling with this issue and trying to determine whether you should put your energy into developing such partnerships and, more specifically, whether you should accept money from the pharmaceutical industry for your organization.

This may help to shed a little more light on your decision. It does not proport to be a definitive, unbiased look at the question. The pharmaceutical industry has enormous budgets to tell the public why partnerships with them are a good thing for women's health organizations. The perspective offered here is intended as an antidote to what has been offered by the industry, at the same time respecting that many groups will choose to enter into partnerships with the industry. This booklet will look at groups who have made the decision to accept money and sponsorship agreements and others which have not.

Why just women's health groups? We decided to narrow the focus because women have a particular relationship to drugs which makes some of their issues unique. Women are often the specific target for advertising by pharmaceutical companies, either because of particular conditions which only women experience (e.g. related to their reproductive functions) or because women are most often the ones in their families who make decisions about what over-the-counter drugs are best for their family members. They visit doctors more often than men (either for themselves or for other family members) and therefore are more likely to be prescribed drugs, and to have prescriptions filled (or not). They are prescribed mood-altering drugs at a higher rate than men. As the sole users of most birth control products—one of the pharmaceutical industry's most lucrative markets - they are often faced with difficult decisions about the safety and efficacy of their choices. As the primary caregivers of sick family members, they are more likely to see the effects – both positive and negative - of prescription and over-the-counter drugs. Women often know "stories" of other women who have had bad experiences with a particular medication, and are more likely to have read magazine and newspaper articles about medication which has been helpful for particular conditions.

In short, we have a relationship to this issue which is specific to us because we are women. Because of the legacy of harmful drugs and devices such as DES, Thalidomide and the Dalkon Shield, North American women in particular have become increasingly wary about the decisions they make in relation to prescription drugs. A more cautious attitude to the idea of "wonder drugs" now prevails. At the same time, the pharmaceutical industry has increased its efforts to appeal to the public to sell their products and a pill-popping mentality prevails in our society a way it never has before.

A Common Scenario

A women's health organization in a large Canadian city has been offering useful information and support to women who have been diagnosed with a particular disease or disorder. Users of this service indicate that they are grateful for this service which has helped them to make difficult decisions about treatment options, talk to other women with the disease and feel like they can get on with the rest of their life.

The organization has been operating on small government grants for the past five years. This has enabled them to keep one staff person—a coordinator—running the organization and training volunteers. Small amounts of money are also raised through an annual direct appeal fundraising campaign and a small fee charged for the production of their quarterly newsletter, but this income alone could not keep the organization afloat. The co-ordinator spends a good deal of her time writing grant applications to keep the service running.

The organization has just learned that their source of government funding is about to dry up due to extensive cutbacks in the health and social services in their province. A member of the board of directors of the organization brings a plan to the board and staff member. She has a good friend who works for Drug Company X, manufacturers of a drug frequently used by women with this disease. This friend has been telling her that she knows her company would give money to help out the service—they just have to say how much they need. The board member presenting this thinks it is a good idea. The board is torn. Opinions vary widely.

Responses to the Issue

"It's a win-win situation—they get to feel better because they're doing some thing that makes them look good, and we have money to keep our service running. What can be wrong with that?"

"I think we should just take the money wherever we can get it. It's the only way we'll keep this service alive. We can't afford to be purists."

"What do you mean?—'It's dirty money?' Isn't all money dirty money?"

"Isn't this just free publicity for the company?"

"This same company also manufactures pesticides which have been shown to contribute to this disease. Why would we want to endorse that?"

"If we take their money, we're turning our backs on all the women who object to this type of sponsorship, women who feel they've been harmed more than helped by the pharmaceutical industry."

"Most women just want the help. They don't really care where the money comes from."

"Taking their money means we're endorsing their product and a band-aid solution for the disease. We put all of our energy into trying to convince government to focus on prevention. Isn't this a bit hypocritical of us?"

"If we say no to an offer like this, we're turning our backs on all those women who need help."

"They've told us there's no strings attached to this money and they seem to be willing to stick to that. Their attitude seems to be "hands off". Why should we doubt that?"

Let's take a closer look at some of the comments made by the board members and staff:

It's a win-win situation—they get to feel better because they're doing something that makes them look good, and we have money to keep our service running. What can be wrong with that?

On the surface, this scenario does indeed look like a win-win situation. And some groups will come to the decision to take the money and not only be quite comfortable with that decision but be able to put the money to good use. Their members will benefit and the drug company will be able to say it has done a good deed with their donation.

A representative from a group for women with AIDS who spoke at our panel discussion described their decision to accept pharmaceutical money: "We are happy to take money from drug companies and turn it into Vitamin C for women with HIV and AIDS." The money they have received from the industry has allowed them to offer programs which they feel they could not otherwise offer. She also pointed out that the survival of her group members is partially linked to the drugs they take, so they have always had a close relationship with the drug industry. She pays about $2,000 for her drugs and says she is glad to see herself and other HIV positive women "get some of that money back" through a donation from the company which manufactures their drugs.

On the other hand, others feel that it may look like a win-win situation but the winning is mostly by the pharmaceutical company. One panellist, who had canvassed reps from some of the manufacturers of the most commonly prescribed drugs for women's reproductive conditions, learned that most donations to women's health groups (and other non-profit health organizations) come from the marketing budget of a company. In most cases, donations must be linked to a product line of that particular company. Therefore, you would not likely see a company which does not manufacture for example, a fertility medication , giving money to an infertility support group, and similarly, companies which manufacture fertility medication would specifically target infertility groups for their donations.

The industry has much to gain from making such donations and forming such links.

1)Association with a reputable organization can provide a more credible endorsement of their product than if the promotion were coming directly from the industry (i.e the goodwill associated with a company's name when they are seen to be making contributions to groups can have a direct impact in the public's mind about the value of their products).

2) If a company is in the pre-launch phase of the introduction of a new drug, they can use the captive audience of the group they have funded to spread awareness about their drug and about the disease which the drug is treating. Funding an organization to provide educational outreach about a disease such as osteoporosis serves to raise the general public's awareness of this issue and, importantly for the drug company, of drug treatments which are being developed to treat it.

3) 0If they are seeking approval from regulatory bodies for a drug which they have manufactured, they can use their funded groups to help them argue for the need for approval of this drug.

Some groups may conclude that the concerns pointed out here simply are not a problem for them. As with the women and AIDS group above, their need of that contribution outweighed any moral concerns they had about the issue of accepting industry money, although their decision was not reached without considerable discussion and debate.

There is, however, one way in which industry wins and the recipient of their money can lose: support from the industry dulls criticism. The National Women's Health Network in the United States, for example, has developed a policy not to take money from the pharmaceutical industry because one of the foundations of their educational work is to encourage women to seek alternatives to pills and surgery in dealing with their health problems, and to look at the social and economic reasons behind much ill health. Promoting education and prevention as cornerstones to improved health, they have worked hard to wean women off of the "pill for every ill" mentality so prevalent in western society. While they also recognize the need for medication in many situations, they have also helped raise awareness about the ways that some medications have done more harm than good to women. This focus runs completely contradictory to a motive of increased profits for the pharmaceutical industry.

I think we should just take the money wherever we can get it. It's the only way we'll keep this service alive. We can't afford to be purists.

This is a commonly held opinion. Many groups are dealing with the sheer logistics of survival and staying alive and feel they can't afford to look a gift horse in the mouth.

Although hard to look at, it might be worth asking, 'Is this really the *only* way you'll keep this service alive?' Frequently the option of pharmaceutical money comes to groups without a lot of effort. The industry is looking to make partnerships such as this and in the larger scheme of things, offering money to a community based women's health organization to keep its doors open represents a drop in the bucket of their profits. Groups are often surprised when after years of hounding philanthropic organizations and individual donors for money, the offer for money from a pharmaceutical company comes to them almost effortlessly. Understandably, this is enormously appealing to anyone who is sick and tired of trying to raise money. But it might be worth asking, if this came so effortlessly, is it the only money that might be gotten without much struggle?

What do you mean?—'It's dirty money?' Isn't all money dirty money?

The term "dirty money" has been used to describe money which may have been used for less than honourable purposes. Some people have argued that there is no difference between taking money from the pharmaceutical companies and accepting money from banks, insurance companies or other large corporations. The argument goes that those companies or financial institutions which may appear to have no strings attached to their money may also be funding practices or manufacturing products (particularly in Third World countries) which your group would find ethically questionable.

For example, one group was considering approaching Shopper's Drug Mart (a large chain of pharmacies across Canada) for a donation to its awareness campaign on women's cancers. After doing some research into the company's background and holdings, they discovered that Shoppers Drug Mart is owned by the Imperial Tobacco Company. This group chose not to pursue funding from Shoppers since it felt compromised in being involved – even indirectly - with manufacturers of a cancer-causing substance. Another organization agreed to accept a donation from Shopper's Drug Mart providing the money was not perceived to come directly from Imperial Tobacco, requiring that the cheque be made out by Shopper's.

Isn't this just free publicity for the company?

In Canada, discussions are underway between the federal government and representatives of the pharmaceutical industry to consider allowing the industry the right to advertise prescription drugs directly to the public. At present they can only advertise directly to physicians, usually done through direct mail, in advertisements in medical journals and through representatives of the industry. Direct-to-consumer advertising is already allowed in the United States meaning that one commonly finds advertisements for birth control, mood-altering drugs and other compounds available only through prescription from a doctor in such everyday places as magazines, radio and television.

Because Canada currently has a prohibition against direct-to-consumer advertising (a prohibition which health care advocates are arguing strongly to maintain), the pharmaceutical industry seeks out other ways to reach the consumer directly about their products without having to go through the intermediary of the doctor.

If your organization does choose to accept money from a pharmaceutical company which manufactures a product which members of your group may use, it is worth keeping in mind that you are indirectly providing endorsement of that company and their product through your action. It is in the company's best interest to have this endorsement of their product from a non-commercial source.

Similarly, if the company funding you is developing a new product for your user group (e.g. a fertility drug in the case of an infertility group) your group may unwittingly become the focus for promotion of this drug by the company. The group may become a conduit of information for the company to the potential users of the drug. In the case of a drug which is badly needed and has been properly tested, this may not be such a bad thing. In the case of a drug which the manufacturers are trying to fast-track through the government approval process, or a drug which is simply a copy-cat of another product on the market, the relationship becomes a little more questionable.

Some groups may be quite comfortable with this while others may not. Each group must come to its own conclusions about what role they may want to play —either directly or indirectly—in promoting a company and its product. Some groups go as far as outright promotion of a product in exchange for funding. For example, the Crohn's and Colitis Foundation of Canada agreed to have their organization's name printed on the product labelling for Imodium, an anti-diarrheal drug. The packaging includes the message: "Proud Sponsor of the Crohn's and Colitis Foundation of Canada".

If you are accepting money, you may want to be very clear from the start what the parameters of that relationship are and get it in writing. As a minimum, the company should be made to understand clearly that it cannot influence the advice a group gives its members, nor can it use the members as targets for promotion of their products.

This same company also manufactures pesticides which have been shown to contribute to this disease. Why would we want to endorse that?

In part from pressure from environmental and health activists, more research is slowly being done into the links between cancer and toxins in the environment, such as pesticides. As women's health groups probe further into this, we have been disturbed to find that sometimes the very companies which are manufacturing cancer therapy are also producing toxic pesticides which may be contributing to cancer in the first place. For example, Zeneca, the manufacturers of tamoxifen citrate earn $470 million each year marketing this cancer therapy drug, at the same time as it earns $300 million each year from sales of the carcinogenic herbicide acetochlor (Elisabeth Rosenthal, "Maker of Cancer Drugs to Oversee Prescriptions at 11 Cancer Clinics, *New York Times,* April 15, 1997, section A, pg. 1.) Further, a paint company subsidiary of Zeneca has been held responsible for 30% of all the toxic chemicals dumped into the St. Lawrence River (Monte Paulsen, quoted in Jim Hightower, *There's Nothing in the Middle of the Road But Yellow Stripes and Dead Armadillos ,* New York: HarperCollins, 1997, pgs. 215-216, cited in *Rachel's Environment and Health Weekly,* #571, Nov 6, 1997).

As one member of the audience at our panel discussion put it: "They're killing us on one side and curing us on the other and making money both ways!"

The women's health movement and more recently the breast cancer awareness movement has long purported prevention as one of the main tenets of its outreach and advocacy efforts. When links are found between potential funders and the causes of the diseases the groups are fighting, this is often a connection many are not prepared to live with.

When considering funding from a pharmaceutical company, it is always helpful to do some background research on the products the company manufacturers. This information is easily found on the Internet, in public libraries and in the company's annual reports.

If we take their money, we're turning our backs on all the women who object to this type of sponsorship, women who feel they've been harmed more than helped by the pharmaceutical industry.

There is no question that the products of the pharmaceutical industry help countless people worldwide to both stay alive and to live a better quality of life. Nevertheless, in its aim to increase its profits, the industry has *also* manufactured products which have seriously harmed many women, usually due to improper initial testing.

One such example is DES (diethylstilbestrol) a synthetic form of the hormone estrogen which was given to millions of pregnant women in both the developed and developing world between the 1940s and the 1970s in the belief that it could prevent miscarriage. Instead it was found to not only be ineffective in preventing miscarriage but was also found to cause serious harm to many of the children (both daughters and sons) of those women who took it. Many daughters of the women developed a range of problems in their reproductive organs, including a rare form of vaginal cancer generally not found in young women.

Regrettably, in spite of volumes of scientific evidence, the companies which manufactured DES until it was banned for use in pregnancy in the 1970s, have denied any negligence and instead have paid out millions of dollars in the settlement of lawsuits against them. Further, they have done nothing to notify the millions of mothers, daughters and sons around the world who were harmed by the drug to ensure that they are receiving proper follow-up care. Instead this responsibility has fallen in the hands of the women who were harmed by the drug in the first place. Organizations such as DES Action, with chapters in most of the developed countries where the drug was prescribed, exist to inform the public about the history of this drug and the need for close medical surveillance of those exposed to it.

Groups such as DES Action have taken strong positions against accepting money from the pharmaceutical industry because of the negligence they have displayed with drugs like DES. DES Action Canada, for example, has publicly stated that they will have nothing to do with the particular companies which manufactured the drug unless the following conditions are met:

1) that the company publicly acknowledge that DES has caused health problems in the mothers and their children, including cancer and reproductive/fertility problems;

2) that the company publicize the ill effects of DES in order to locate all the DES exposed mothers and children in Canada;

3) that the company compensate all the DES-exposed who have been harmed by the drug.

The experience of DES strongly influenced the women's health movement worldwide to take a close look at the pharmaceutical industry. As a result, women working for women's health have led campaigns to press for a more careful review of our drug approval process, and in particular, have argued against the approval of particular drugs whose long-term safety has been questioned, such as some injectable contraceptives.

It is wise to keep in mind that a decision of whether or not to be involved with the pharmaceutical industry is not one taken without an historical context for this issue and one which has a particularly problematic legacy.

Most women just want the help. They don't really care where the money comes from.

This may be very true for a number of women and for many organizations. Certainly when we are dealing with diseases such as cancer, it is often the case that people will "do anything" to get help or get access to a new treatment, whatever the emotional or financial cost.

Staff members and members of boards have a duty to make fair and ethical decisions on behalf of their members or clients. A group may choose to use this time of decision-making as an opportunity to raise awareness about a number of related issues: 1) the role the pharmaceutical industry plays in our lives and the extent to which we have become a drug-dependent pill-popping culture; 2) to involve members in the political process occurring in Canada around the restructuring of our Health Protection Branch; or 3) arrange an evening with speakers form women's health organizations who have taken strong stands on this issue (e.g. DES Action or an AIDS organization).

Admittedly the consciousness-raising route is not for everyone. Some groups simply do not have the time or the inclination. One Ontario-based breast cancer organization canvassed its members through a mailed questionnaire asking for their thoughts on accepting money from pharmaceutical companies before they developed their board policy on this issue.

There is no one correct prescription for everyone on this issue. Each group must decide for itself which is the best route to go.

Taking their money means we're endorsing their product and a band-aid solution for the disease. We put all of our energy into trying to convince government to focus on prevention. Isn't this a bit hypocritical of us?

There is no question that many products of the pharmaceutical industry help countless people worldwide to both stay alive and to live a better quality of life. Nevertheless, in its aim to increase its profits, the industry has also manufactured products which have seriously harmed many women, usually due to improper initial testing.

One such example is DES (diethylstilbestrol) a synthetic form of the hormone estrogen which was given to millions of pregnant women in both the developed and developing world between the 1940s and the 1970s in the belief that it could prevent miscarriage. Instead it was found to not only be ineffective in preventing miscarriage but was also found to cause serious harm to many of the children (both daughters and sons) of those women who took it. Many daughters of the women developed a range of problems in their reproductive organs, including a rare form of vaginal cancer generally not found in young women.

Regrettably, in spite of volumes of scientific evidence, the companies which manufactured DES until it was banned for use in pregnancy in the 1970s, have denied any negligence and instead have paid out millions of dollars in the settlement of lawsuits against them. (Note that DES was only banned in 1970 in some parts of the world, mainly the US and western Europe. It is still being sold over the counter in a number of developing countries and some parts of Eastern Europe.)

Further, the companies which manufactured the drug have done nothing to notify the millions of mothers, daughters and sons around the world who were harmed by the drug to ensure that they are receiving proper follow-up care. Instead this responsibility has fallen in the hands of the women who were harmed by the drug in the first place. Organizations such as DES Action, with chapters in most of the developed countries where the drug was prescribed, exist to inform the public about the history of this drug and the need for close medical surveillance of those exposed to it.

Groups such as DES Action have taken strong positions against accepting money from the pharmaceutical industry because of the negligence it has displayed with drugs like DES. DES Action Canada, for example, has publicly stated that they will not engage in any dealings with the particular companies which manufactured the drug unless the following conditions are met:

1) that the company publicly acknowledge that DES has caused health problems in the mothers

and their children, including cancer and reproductive/fertility problems;

2) that the company publicize the ill effects of DES in order to locate all the DES exposed mothers and children in Canada;

3) that the company compensate all the DES-exposed who have been harmed by the drug.
To strengthen their point regarding negligence, DES Action, in fact, has a position of taking no money from any pharmaceutical companies, not just those which manufactured DES.

The experience of DES strongly influenced the women's health movement worldwide to take a close look at the pharmaceutical industry. As a result, women working for women's health have led campaigns to press for a more careful review of our drug approval process, and in particular, have argued against the approval of particular drugs whose long-term safety has been questioned, such as some injectable contraceptives.

It is wise to keep in mind that a decision of whether or not to be involved with the pharmaceutical industry is a decision which is taken within an historical context. The context is one which has a particularly problematic legacy.

They've told us there's no strings attached to this money and they seem to be willing to stick to that. Their attitude seems to be "hands off." Why should we doubt that?

One women's health organizer looking at this issue for her organization, commented, "There are strings, but they are strings of gossamer", meaning there are strings but you can't always see them.

The point is made best by Barbara Mintzes, in a publication for Health Action International, Blurring the Boundaries: "Any patient group, charity or institution with financial links to the industry or a specific company which spreads awareness of a disease so that more people may seek drug treatment, endorses specific products, or presents positively biased drug information is helping to promote product sales" (p. 26).

It is important to remember that industry's motivations for giving money to an organization are not philanthropic in nature. They give money to targeted groups in targeted fields which relate to their product lines.

Groups may find themselves in this situation unwittingly. The original overture from a drug company may have come from a perfectly well-intentioned individual who cared about their group. Companies are made up of individuals, and individuals of all companies would like to feel they work for a business which is a good corporate citizen. As much as companies wish to buy good will, staff in drug companies also pressure their employers to make donations to community based organizations they feel committed to. Although the donation may come from marketing and all that that involves, the original impetus may not.

Similarly, most researchers who work for pharmaceutical companies come directly from university or have been recruited from a research project. Most of them begin their career with good intentions of hoping to "cure" diseases. While the company as an entity is concerned with profit, the individuals lower down the hierarchy are not always so motivated. Contacts between individuals from a pharmaceutical company and a community organization can be made with the best of intentions by the initial individuals. Later the group may be taken by surprise when the company indicates they would like a higher level of public recognition or sponsorship or indicates they don't like the way in which their product or the whole industry is portrayed in the group's literature.

One thing your group can do is talk to other community organizations which have accepted money from or engaged in some sort of partnership with that same company. Find out what their experience has been in working with that company. For example, the Infertility Network (Canada), which has received funds from Organon and Serono, agreed to have their name added to a brochure about infertility produced by Serono. The Executive Director noted "This was important to them [the company], but it helped raise our profile and so it suited our purposes to do it." Another group might feel compromised by the same experience. Each organization has their own story to tell.

If Your Group Decides to Take the Money…

David Gilbert, in his paper, "Much to gain, more to lose", suggests that there are six questions a group can ask itself when considering this issue: 1) Do we need to accept funding from a company? 2) What do we seek to gain from such an arrangement? 3) What are our views on the use of medicines for the patients we purport to represent - what do the patients think (i.e. attitudes to care and treatment choice issues)? 4) What are our views on the nature of the industry? 5) What are the alternatives to company funding? and 6) What are the risks of such arrangements?

We can learn from the experience of other organizations who have worked through this issue. The following are some general guidelines culled from the May '97 panel discussion and from other groups consulted since then about how to proceed when entering into sponsorship agreements with a pharmaceutical company or in accepting money from them.

1) If you are a newly-formed group or one which has not yet dealt with this issue, it is probably best to assume that you will be confronted with it at some point. Most groups find it helpful to develop a written policy on the subject and to make the policy known to your members. The policy may be as formal as being a part of your by-laws or, more commonly, a general policy of the organization. Some treat it as a separate policy while others include it as part of their overall policy on corporate donations.

2) Be very clear with any newly-hired or volunteer fundraiser what your group's policy is on this issue. Be as specific as possible with anyone doing this work on your behalf (e.g. "We will not consider funds from individual pharmaceutical companies but will consider accepting funds from pharmaceutical organizations," "We will consider all types of funds, regardless of their source," "We will not take money from any organization which manufactures substances which have been linked to cancer," "We will consider money from companies which have made a strong public statement and put money behind the advancement of women," etc.)

3) When dealing with representatives from a pharmaceutical company who may potentially give your group money, you may want to consider, as some groups have, only meeting on your "turf", i.e. not meeting at their offices, and having a policy not to accept free meals or other freebies as part of the discussion. The point is to maintain control of the discussion and not to be beholden to them, whatever your group's decision may be.

4) Be sure that any arrangements entered into with a pharmaceutical company are documented and copies are kept in your files and sent to the donor. These can take the form of a letter of agreement outlining what your terms are (e.g. "We agree to use this money responsibly but/and agree/do not agree to enter into the promotion of Company X's product," "We agree/do not

agree to carry the company's logo on our printed materials.") Be as clear as possible about your intent. Possibilities left open to interpretation may not always work in your group's best interest. The National Osteoporosis Society of Great Britain has developed very clear guidelines relating to any liaison between their organization and pharmaceutical companies and their agents (see Resources section below).

5) Your group may wish to only agree to take money which has been put in a blind trust controlled by an independent board, to avoid any possible influence.

6) You owe it to your membership and anyone who supports your group to be as transparent as possible. If you have accepted money from a pharmaceutical company, be sure to acknowledge it in publications, annual reports and at public meetings.

The author wishes to thank the following people for their input: Theresa Dobko (Canada), David Gilbert (UK), Lisa Hayes (Netherlands), Joel Lexchin (Canada), Peter Mansfield (Australia), Barbara Mintzes (Canada), & Ellen 't Hoen (France).

Further Reading on This and Related Topics

Blurring the Boundaries: New Trends in Drug Promotion by Barbara Mintzes for HAI-Europe, 1998.

Statement of the Working Group on Transparency and Accountability in Drug Regulation, Health Action International and the Dag Hammarskjold Foundation, 1996.

Rachel's Environment and Health Weekly, weekly newsletter available from Environmental Research Foundation, P.O. Box 5036, Annapolis, Maryland 21403, Fax (410) 263-8944; Internet: <u>erf@rachel.org</u>, or on the Internet: http://www.monitor.net/rachel/.

The ties that bind: Drug industry sponsorship by Lisa Hayes and Barbara Mintzes in HAI-Lights (newsletter of Health Action International), Vol. 2, No. 2-3, July/August 1997.

Much to gain, more to lose? The perils of partnership between patient groups and the pharmaceutical industry, by David Gilbert, unpublished paper available from the author, c/o Office for Public Management, 252b Gray's Inn Road, London, UK, W1X 8JT.

New trends in drug promotion, by David Gilbert and Andrew Chetley in Consumer Policy Review, Vol. 6, No. 5, 1996: 165.

Commercial sponsorsip and NGOs, statement available from the European Public Health Alliance, 33 rue de Pascale, B-1040 Bruxelles, Belgique, fax: (+322) 231-0990, e-mail epha@club.innet.be.

Other Resources

For a copy of their guidelines on this topic:

National Osteoporosis Society,
PO Box 10,
Radstock, Bath, BA3 3YB, UK
Tel: 01761 471771

For the HAI publications listed above:
Health Action International - Europe
Jacob van Lennepkade 334-T 1053 NJ
Amsterdam, The Netherlands
Tel (+31-20) 683-3684
Fax: (+31-20) 685-5002
e-mail: hai@hai.antenna.nl

Resources for Researching Specific Pharmaceutical Companies

EthicScan, P.O. Box 54034, Toronto, Ontario, M6A 3B7, Canada. Tel: 416-783-6776, Fax: 416-783-7386, e-mail: ethic@concentric.net, Internet: www.ethicscan.on.ca.

For a fee—reduced for non-profit organizations—EthicScan offers detailed information on the ethical profiles of many Canadian pharmaceutical companies.

Rachel's Environment and Health Weekly is a weekly publication available electronically or by mail, which covers a wide range of environmental and corporate issues. An electronic search will bring up anything they have published on questions relating to the environmental practices of specific corporations.

Available from: Environmental Research Foundation, P.O. Box 5036, Annapolis, Maryland 21403 Fax (410) 263-8944; e-mail: erf@rachel.org, or on the Internet: www.monitor.net/rachel.

The Multinational Monitor is published monthly except bimonthly in January/February and July/August by Essential Information, Inc. The Multinational Monitor tracks corporate activity, especially in the Third World, focusing on the export of hazardous substances, worker health and safety, labor union issues and the environment.

To contact: Multinational Monitor, PO Box 19405, Washington, DC 20036 e-mail: monitor@essential.org, Internet: www.essential.org/monitor/monitor.html.

Communicating About Risks and Infant Feeding
Advocacy Tools

PENNY VAN ESTERIK, DEPARTMENT OF ANTHROPOLOGY, YORK UNIVERSITY
WORLD ALLIANCE FOR BREASTFEEDING ACTION (WABA)

During the process of writing and circulating *Risks, Rights and Regulation: Communicating about Risks and Infant Feeding* (see Volume One), a number of advocacy tools were produced. The first, "Breastfeeding and the Environment," drafted during a workshop in Toronto in November 1999, reflected the views of a variety of stakeholders. The workshop was attended by interested representatives from: Women's Network on Health and Environment; National Network on Environments and Women's Health; La Leche League, Canada; Toronto Public Health; International Lactation Consultants Association (ILCA); Stop Cancer; UNICEF, Canada; Breastfeeding Committee of Canada; South Riverdale Community Health Centre; Multiracial Network for Environmental Justice; and the Medical Reform Group, in addition to interested faculty and students. The handout was circulated informally and generated discussion about how different groups might want to approach (or avoid) the subject of breastmilk and chemical residues.

The second document, "The IBFAN Guideline Statement on Breastfeeding and Dioxins," was developed and circulated widely in 2000. IBFAN (International Baby Food Action Network) groups have been working for many years with ecological groups in different countries on this topic. In Belgium, Bulgaria, and Luxembourg for example, good working relations have been built up over the years with these groups. The aim of their collaboration is to counter the use of breastmilk as a yardstick for measuring pollution in their national campaigns. The IBFAN statement of December 20, 2000 is a guideline for groups and is meant to be adapted to national and local conditions. This statement was developed by the IBFAN working group on Contaminants in Baby Foods, translated from French, and reviewed by the toxicologists of the International Programme on Chemical Safety at the World Health Organization.

The third document, "Working Together for a Toxic-Free Future," was developed with the World Alliance for Breastfeeding Action (WABA), the Pesticide Action Network (PAN), and the International POPs Elimination Network (IPEN). Wording had to be carefully negotiated between breastfeeding groups and environmental groups. Working together across different agendas requires both trust and trade-offs. The joint statement by participating organizations of WABA and IPEN went through many versions- gradually expanding beyond its one page format to more than four pages, and eventually contracting down to a single page. Even with several face-to-face meetings and six months of email consultation, not all groups consulted were willing to endorse the statement. The statement attests to the willingness of groups to set aside their differences to reach common goals - to reduce the chemical contamination is us all.

The fourth document, "Towards Healthy Environments for Children: Frequently Asked Questions (FAQ) About Breastfeeding in a Contaminated Environment" was drafted first within the breastfeeding movement to begin to address the concerns of mothers who may be bombarded with information about the effects of chemical contamination on their bodies, but have no satisfactory answers on how to make decisions about infant feeding. It is clearly more realistic and informative than the initial document produced by the Toronto workshop in 1999. The document was extensively reviewed and revised in 2003, and as of October 2003 has been endorsed by several international breastfeeding and environmental groups. The document is now being distributed through WHO.

Breastfeeding and the Environment

We live in a polluted world. Women, men and children are all affected by environmental pollutants, and many of them are linked to cancer. While everyone should avoid building up a body burden of contaminants, women have the potential for sharing their body burden of chemical contaminants with their children.

Mother's milk is a symbol for all that is pure, reliable, sustaining and dependable - a gift of inestimable value. In the last decade, public health messages about the benefits of breastfeeding for both mothers and infant have been heard alongside warnings that breastmilk is threatened by the widespread pollution of our environment. Toxic substances such as PCBs, dioxins, pesticides, phthalates and heavy metals have been found in samples of breastmilk from some women in some places. However, no adverse effects on growth or occurrences of illnesses in the first year of life have been attributed to the presence of these chemicals in human milk. One of the most authoritative reference texts on this subject, Chemical Compounds in Human Milk, by A. Jensen and S. Slorach (1991: 288) concludes:

> Reports in the mass media about the presence of toxic chemicals in breastmilk often alarm mothers, who wonder whether they should get their milk analysed and, if the levels are relatively high, stop breastfeeding. Virtually all national and international expert committees have hitherto concluded—on the basics of available information—that the benefits of breastfeeding outweigh the possible risks from contaminants present in human milk at normal levels. There is little point in investigating milk from individual concerned mothers, unless there are indications of abnormally heavy exposure, for example, at the workplace or due to poisoning incidents.

Environmental contamination enters our bodies from many different sources—air, water, food, with the result that people have to choose between unacceptable options about their food they eat and feed their children, the drugs they take and the air they breathe. We do not find it acceptable to poison ourselves, our children and particularly, our infants when industries can and should be required to phase out and eliminate chemicals that pose a risk to human health and the environment.

Toxins are found all through the food chain. For example, artificial breastmilk substitutes made from cow's milk or soy are associated with another set of risks, particularly, if they are reconstituted from tap water. Milk-based infant formula has been contaminated by bacteria, radioactivity, chemicals and foreign bodies. Phytoestrogens, high aluminium content, and the use of genetically modified soy in soy-based infant formula are also causes for concern. Environmental pollution is not just a breastfeeding issue. It is everyone's concern. Breastfeeding advocates belong at the forefront of efforts to clean up the environment. Infant feeding is unique because infants rely on one food—milk—for many months of rapid development, while adults have a more varied diet. Women have the right to know that the breastmilk they produce is as pure as it can be. By making reduction of environmental pollution a priority, conditions can be improved. WABA joins the members of the International POPs Elimination Network (IPEN) in calling for a quick ratification of the Stockholm Convention on POPs.

In the short term, breastfeeding mothers may want to take the following personal actions to make breastfeeding even safer:

- select food from lower on the food chain

- eat organic fruits and vegetables

- wash and peel fruits and vegetables

- remove skin from chicken

- limit consumption of fatty meats and dairy products

- avoid crash dieting while breastfeeding

- eat small fish such as sardines rather than large fish

- avoid eating fish from polluted lakes

- reduce use of toxic household cleaners

- avoid contact with pesticides at work and at home

- avoid smoke.

However, long term solutions require political actions:

- link breastfeeding, environmental, and cancer prevention groups

- lobby for international conventions such as the WHO/UNICEF Code for the Marketing of Breastmilk Substitutes, and international treaties to eliminate POPs

- explore the possibility that standards for tolerable levels of pollutants should be lower for girls and women

- set workplace safety standards suitable for pregnant and lactating women

- make cleaning up our food supply and the environment a priority for all levels of government.

December 20th, 2000

In recent weeks there have been an increasing number of reports in the press about the problems caused by dioxins.

Dioxins are produced during various industrial processes, particularly during burning and incineration. They are environmental contaminants and are found mainly in the food chain where they are absorbed by humans. Dioxins are stored in body fat and are extremely persistent. Absorption takes place mainly through the food we eat (90-95%) but also through the air we breathe (5-10%). Breastmilk is often cited as a source of dioxins—but this is because fat soluble contaminants are relatively easily measured in breastmilk, not because breastmilk is any more contaminated than other body parts.

A recent review noted that studies have shown that the effects of dioxin contamination were associated with exposure via the placenta rather than via breastmilk. In areas of high contamination levels due to industrial processes or accidents, the available scientific literature indicates that a high level of dioxin contamination during pregnancy can lead to the impairment of child growth and development. Importantly however, it was concluded that breastfeeding, even in a contaminated environment, has a positive impact on the development of children as compared to those artificially fed (1).

As a result of these findings, a number of countries have advocated that breastfeeding should continue to be "encouraged and promoted on the basis of convincing evidence of its benefits to the overall health and development of the infant." (2).

The International Baby Food Action Network (IBFAN) agrees with this recommendation and further recommends that the debate about dioxin contamination should not unduly influence a mother's decision to breastfeed.

1. Breastmilk provides optimal, unique and perfectly balanced nutrition for a baby
2. Breastfeeding affords many irreplaceable health advantages for both mother and child
3. Pregnant women and breastfeeding mothers should be alert to the problems caused by chemical contaminants
4. All citizens should work to raise awareness of the dangers of environmental pollution.

IBFAN urgently calls upon decision makers in industry and politics to adopt environmen-tally-friendly initiatives in production and waste-disposal, to promote political awareness of ecological dangers, and to create the appropriate legal framework to prevent the harmful contamination of our environment and to protect the health of our children, both present and future generations.

References

1. Van Leeuwen F.X. R., Younes M.M. Assessment of the health risks of dioxins: Reevaluation of the tolerable daily intake (TDI), *Food Additives and Contaminants* 17 (4),

2. Ministry of Agriculture, Food and Fisheries (1996) Dioxins in human milk, *Food Surveillance Information Sheet*, MAFF, UK

3. National Breastfeeding Commission (1995) Residues in breastmilk, *Bulletin of the Ministry of Health* (Germany), 2/96.

Documents for Further Information

1. WHO Press Office (1999) Dioxins and their effects on human health, Fact Sheet No. 225, June 1999, WHO; Geneva.

2. UNICEF (1997) Breastfeeding and environmental contamination: A discussion paper, Nutrition Section, UNICEF, New York.

3. United States Environmental Protection Agency (EPA) website: http://www.epa.gov/ ncea/dioxin.htm (see Frequently Asked Questions, no. 9, Is it safe to nurse my infant?)

4. Van Leeuwen F. X. R, Younes M. M (1998) Assessment of the health risk of dioxins: Re-evaluation of the tolerable daily intake, *Food Additives and Contaminants* (WHO Regional Office for Europe), Volume 17, No. 4 April 2000 (p. 237).

5. Schutz D, Moy G. G and Käferstein F. K (1998) GEMS/Food International Dietary Survey: Infant exposure to certain organochlorine contaminants from breastmilk: A risk assessment, Food Safety Unit, World Health Organisation, Geneva.

6. www.ibfan.org provides further information on the work of the International Baby Food Action Network (IBFAN). IBFAN is a global network comprising over 150 health and consumer groups in over 90 countries. The aim of IBFAN is to support, protect and promote breastfeeding, to monitor the appropriate marketing and distribution of breastmilk substitutes and complementary foods, and to promote and support timely complementary feeding practices using adequate local food resources.

This statement was developed by the IBFAN working group on Contaminants in Baby Foods in response to media scares on this issue. It was reviewed by members of the IBFAN Co-ordinating Council in November 2000. This statement is intended as a guideline to assist IBFAN groups in preparing a response to press reports and will be shared with other concerned NGOs.

We would like to express our thanks to the toxicologists of the International Programme on Chemical Safety at the World Health Organisation for their valuable comments on this statement.

Call for Endorsement . . .

a joint statement by participating organisations of the World Alliance for Breastfeeding Action (WABA) & International POPs Elimination Network (IPEN)

We share a common concern: Toxic chemicals are contaminating our children

If we tested every infant born today, anywhere in the world, we would find that s/he has a body burden of toxic industrial chemicals. Dioxins, PCBs, mercury, phthalates, pesticides and other dangerous substances are being passed from parent to child as early as the prenatal period.

Tiny doses of these chemicals can have a dramatic effect on the developing child. Levels of mercury that would have no impact on an adult can harm the developing brain of a foetus. A few trillionths of a gram of dioxin and PCBs can damage the developing immune and nervous systems. DDT, PCBs, dioxins and other persistent organic pollutants not only cross the placenta, they also enter into breastmilk.

We recognise the need to promote breastfeeding while we work towards ending the contamination of our communities

The contamination of breastmilk is one symptom of the environmental contamination in our communities. Responsibility for this problem belongs to the industrial sources of contamination, not to breastfeeding women. The individual decision to breastfeed must be promoted and protected while we work collectively towards eliminating the chemicals that contaminate the food we eat, the water we drink, the air we breathe, and the products we use.

Studies have shown that breastfeeding, even in a contaminated environment, has a positive impact on the development of children as compared to those who are artificially fed. Breastfeeding supports infant growth and health as well as maternal health in ways that breastmilk substitutes cannot. Indeed, breastmilk contains sub-stances that help the child develop a stronger immune system and other protections against environmental pollutants and pathogens.

Therefore, educational and advocacy efforts to promote a toxic-free future for our children should recognise, encourage and support collective actions aimed at promoting breastfeeding, reducing chemical contamination and developing the strongest possible pollution prevention laws.

We share a vision of a toxic-free future and generations of healthy children

In Sweden, strong governmental programmes to eliminate persistent organic pollutants like DDT, dieldrin, PCBs and dioxin have resulted in dramatic decreases in contaminants in breastmilk. In the United States, bans on lead in gasoline and smoking in public places have resulted in dramatic decreases in the levels of dangerous chemicals in the blood of young children. These public health achieve-ments show that reductions in the production, use and disposal of toxic chemicals, along with the destruction of toxic chemical stockpiles and reservoirs, can decrease the body burden in our children and in all of us. The United Nations Stockholm Convention on Persistent Organic Pollutants (POPs), the development of sustainable alternatives to dioxin-producing incineration, local and national efforts to restrict the use of pesticides or to phase out the uses and emissions of mercury, all deserve our energetic and sustained support.

We pledge to work together towards the day when our infants are born toxin free, and can grow and develop in a toxic-free world.

Updated list of Endorsers, July 2002

Agenda for Environment and Responsible Development, Tanzania • Alaska Community Action on Toxics, USA • Alianza por Una Mejor Calidad de Vida, Chile • Aminingshjälpen (The Swedish Nursing Mothers' Support Group) • Aquamedia, Republic of Georgia • Armenian Centre of Hygiene & Epidemiological Surveillance • Armenian Women for Health and a Healthy Environment • ARNIKA Association, Czech Republic • Arugaan, Philippines • Asociación Argentina de Medivos por el Medio Ambiente (AAMMA), Argentina • Associação de Combate aos Pops (ACPO), Brazil • Associação de Consciência à Prevenção Ocupacional, Brazil • Baby Friendly Hospital Initiative Hong Kong Association (BFHIHKA) • Bangladesh Breastfeeding Foundation (BBF) • Basel Action Network (BAN), Washington, USA • Breastfeeding Information Bureau, Malaysia • Breastfeeding Mothers Support Group (BSMG), Singapore • Breastfeeding Promotion Network of India (BPNI) • Breastfeeding Support Group of Thailand • California Nurses-Midwives Association, USA • Canadian Association of Physicians for the Environment (CAPE) • Cancer Action New York, USA • Chemicals Weapons Working Group, Kentucky, USA • Chris Mulford, IBCLC, USA • Collectif de lutte contre les organochlorés (Joint Action Group against POPs), Quebec, Canada • Common Ground, Kentucky, USA • Commonweal, USA • Community Against Toxics, Cheshire, UK • Consumers International Regional Office for Asia and the Pacific (CI-ROAP) • Coordination Française pour l'Allaitement Maternel (CoFAM), France • Cynthia Pang, IBCLC, Singapore • Department of the Planet Earth, USA • Development Indian Ocean Network (DION), Mauritius • ECO-Accord, Russia • Ecosphere, Belarus • Egyptian Medical Students for Social Responsibility Students, Egypt • Environmental Health Fund, USA • For Civil Society, Kyrghyzstan • Foundation for Realization of Ideas, Belarus • Great Lakes United, New York, USA • Greenpeace International • Greenpeace International Toxics Campaign, Canada • GroundWork, South Africa • HealthCare Without Harm, Washington DC, USA • Indigeneous Environmental Council, Alaska, USA • Information Pour l'Allaitement (IPA), France • Institute for Children's Environmental Health, Washington, USA • International Baby Food Action Network (IBFAN) Penang, Malaysia • International Campaign for Responsible Technology • International Lactation Consultation Association (ILCA) • International Physicians for Prevention of Nuclear War, Egypt • Irish Doctors Environmental Association (IDEA) • Kentucky Environmental Foundation, USA • La Leche League International (LLLI), USA • Marcia Annandale, IBCLC, New Zealand • Movement pour les Droits et le Respect des Générations Futures (MDRGF), France • National Resource Defence Council, USA • National Toxics Network Inc., Australia • New Zealand College of Midwives (NZCOM) • Non-Stockpile Chemical Weapons Citizen Coalition, Kentucky, USA • Pesticide Action Network Asia-Pacific (PANAP) • Pesticide Action Network Central Asia (PANCA) • Pesticide Action Network Germany • Pesticide Action Network North America (PANNA) • Pesticide Action Network UK (PANUK) • Pesticide Action Network, Philippines • Public Interest Consultants, UK z Pusat Penasihat Penyusuan Ibu Malaysia (PPPIM) • Queensland Lactation College, Australia • Red de Acción en Plaguicidas y sus Alternativas de América Latina (RAP-AL), Chile • Red de Acción sobre Plaguicidas y Alternativas en México (RAPAM) • Sandra Steingraber, Teacher, Ecologist, Author of "Living Downstream" & "Having Faith", USA • Sarvodaya Women's Movement, Sri Lanka • Sharyle Patton, International POPs Elimination Network (IPEN) Northern Co-Chair, USA • Srishti, India • Surakshit, India • Sustainable Development Policy Institute (SDPI), Pakistan • Taiwan Watch Institute • Tchala Songolo, CADIC, Congo • Ted Greiner, International Maternal & Child Health (IMCH), Uppsala University, Sweden • Thanal Conservation Action & Information Network (TCAIN), India • The Nordic Workgroup for International Breastfeeeding Issues, Sweden • Toxics Link, India • Virginia Thorley, WABA International Advisory Council member, Australia • WABA Steering Committee • Women in Europe for a Common Future (WECF), Netherlands • Women's Environmental Network, UK • World Information Transfer, USA • Worldwide Fund for Nature/World Wildlife Fund (WWF).

We will update the endorsers list regularly. We welcome your endorsement and also request you to share it with others. This Statement with the latest list of endorsers is available at the WABA & IPEN websites. To endorse, write ASAP to the World Alliance for Breastfeeding Action, WABA, PO.Box 1200, Penang 10850, Malaysia. Fax: 604-6572 655 Email: secr@waba.po.my

This joint statement emerged out of the combined efforts of the participating organisations of WABA & IPEN, in addressing the issue on the contamination of breastmilk and the environment. This collaboration seeks to understand the issue from both the environmental health and justice and breastfeeding perspectives, share experiences and develop communication strategies to educate the general public, health workers, policy makers and the media. It is based on the recognition that breastfeeding promotion should take place alongside efforts to eliminate toxic chemicals from the environment. This statement went through a series of consultations via email discussions and at some key meetings.

The World Alliance for Breastfeeding Action (WABA) is a global people's initiative to protect, promote and support breastfeeding. WABA acts on the Innocenti Declaration targets and works in close liaison with the United Nations Children's Fund (UNICEF). Website: <www.waba.org.br> or <www.waba.org.my> The International POPs Elimination Network (IPEN) is a global network of public interest non-governmental organizations united to work for the global elimination of persistent organic pollutants on an expedited yet socially equitable basis. Website: <www.ipen.org>

Frequently Asked Questions (FAQ) About Breastfeeding in a Contaminated Environment

Should mothers be worried about toxic chemicals in the environment?

Yes; everyone should be worried. Chemical contaminants are causing harm to our children; environmental activists, breastfeeding groups and health advocates worldwide are calling for the elimination of toxic chemicals in the environment. If we were to test infants born today, anywhere in the world, we would find in them a body burden of industrial toxins including dioxins, PCBs, mercury, phthalates, pesticides, flame retardants, bisphenol A and other dangerous substances. These chemicals pass through the placenta and into the fetus during pregnancy, and through breastmilk after birth. Babies and toddlers continue to be exposed to hazardous chemicals through contact with air, water, soil and everyday products such as carpets, clothing, furniture and household products. It is critical that chemical residues be reduced in the environment to reduce both the prenatal and postnatal health risks they pose to infants, children and the general public.

How do chemical residues end up in our bodies and the bodies of our infants?

Many chemicals have the capability to travel far from their sites of origin or use, polluting the air we breathe, the water we consume, the food we eat and the everyday products (such as cosmetics and certain plastics) we touch and use. Some of these chemicals resist metabolic breakdown and excretion, or break down into harmful derivatives that accumulate mainly in our body fat, becoming part of our chemical body burden. Some chemicals act as endocrine disruptors and can damage the reproductive system. No matter where we live or how we live, none of us can avoid being exposed to a wide variety of chemicals and passing on this chemical body burden to the next generation. Children are at higher risk than adults because they are undergoing rapid development and consuming more food in relation to their body weight compared to adults. The only way to reduce their body burden is to eliminate hazardous chemicals from production and use, replacing them with less hazardous chemicals and products.

When does exposure to contaminants start?

Children's exposure to toxic chemicals starts before birth and comes from everything their parents were exposed to—the air they breathed, the food they ate, the products they used and the water they drank. After birth, a child continues to be exposed to chemicals through contact with air, water, soil, food and household items. Even toys and pacifiers may contain harmful chemicals. The biggest impact of pollutants occurs prenatally when the fetus is passing through critical stages of development. Tiny doses of chemical residues can have a dramatic effect on the developing fetus. Levels of mercury that would have little or no impact on an adult can harm the developing fetal brain. Tiny amounts of dioxins and PCBs can damage the developing immune and nervous systems; the phthalate DEHP can disrupt the development of the male reproductive system. Pollutants and heavy metals readily cross the placenta, and some also enter breastmilk.

Why are chemical residues found in breastmilk?

Chemicals accumulate in different body parts including adipose tissue, brain, bone, blood, liver, placenta and semen, and are also found in breastmilk. Chemical residues accumulate in the body fat which is used to produce breastmilk. Because breastmilk is convenient and inexpensive to test for those contaminants stored in body fat, it is often used to monitor human exposure to chemicals that should not be in our bodies. Chemical residues found in breastmilk are like the messenger, the canary in the mine, telling us about the body burdens found in everyone.

Is the presence of these chemical residues in breastmilk a reason not to breastfeed?

No. Exposure before and during pregnancy is a greater risk to the fetus. The existence of chemical residues in breastmilk is not a reason for limiting breastfeeding. In fact, it is a reason to breastfeed because breastmilk contains substances that help the child develop a stronger immune system and gives protection against environmental pollutants and pathogens. Breastfeeding can help limit the damage caused by fetal exposure.

Should breastfeeding mothers have their breastmilk tested?

Breastmilk testing is not necessary unless a mother has been exposed to excessive amounts of chemicals during an industrial accident, or during long periods of workplace exposure involving the mishandling of pesticides, for example. In the case of industrial accidents, public health officials would provide instructions about the best way to minimize risks. Thus, individual testing of breastmilk should never be used as a basis for making decisions about breastfeeding, except in the rare case of an emergency short term response to an industrial accident. Some communities monitor the changing amounts of chemical residues in breastmilk as part of the process of protecting the community. Such monitoring can indicate the need for better protective regulation and indicate the efficacy of previous legislation. For example, contaminants appearing in breastmilk at high levels twenty to thirty years ago alarmed activists and politicians. The regulations and legislation that followed resulted in slowly diminishing the amount of these chemical residues in our bodies. This clearly shows the benefits and necessity for strong protective laws and regulations, and for their enforcement and monitoring. Monitoring may also reveal the presence of toxic chemicals not previously considered to be capable of lodging in human tissue. In some communities, mothers may provide breastmilk as part of an effort to provide accurate information to guide environmental policy. Other communities encourage different means for testing for the presence of chemicals, such as using blood, urine, semen, hair or ear wax.

Can these chemical residues harm our children?

Most health effects on the infant from chemical residues are associated with exposure before conception from damage done to fathers' semen, or when the baby is in the womb, rather than from breastmilk. Most of the damage is done by the time the infant is born. Studies have shown that breastfeeding, even in a contaminated environment, has a positive impact on the development of children as compared to children fed with commercial baby milks. Breastfeeding provides a vast array of physical and psychological benefits to mothers and babies not available to infants fed on commercial products. While there are few health risks from the average levels of chemical residues in breastmilk, lower levels of exposure to toxic chemicals would benefit everyone, especially the developing fetus and the breastfeeding infant.

Are commercial baby milks a safer choice?

No. Even in areas where the contamination is highest, the risks of artificial feeding and not breastfeeding are even greater. There are different contaminants in commercial feeding products, including infant formula, the water in which it is mixed, the containers in which it is stored and often in the bottles used for feeding. Heavy metals such as lead, aluminum, cadmium and mercury, chemical residues from pesticides and fertilizers, and hormonedisrupting plasticizers have all been found in commercial infant foods. Recalls of infant formula from the market are regularly made because of industrial and bacterial contamination; they are not sterile products. Reports and advisories in recent years have warned that infant formula can be contaminated with pathogenic bacteria, after several infants died or became seriously ill from consuming infant formula contaminated by *Enterobacter sakazakii*. In addition, while some common contaminants such as nitrates in ground water may be tolerated when ingested by a breastfeeding mother, they can be fatal if the water is given directly to the baby. The use of genetically engineered ingredients (such as soy in soy-based infant formulas) and the inclusion in infant formula of components produced by genetic modification, pose new and as yet unknown risks. Although these are not chemical contaminants, they underscore the importance of promoting breastfeeding as the healthier choice.

How does the production of infant formula contribute to a polluted environment?

Compared to the natural production of breastmilk, the production of infant formula adds to environmental contamination. The consumption of materials such as fossil fuels, wood products, and other kinds of energy, as well as the clearing of forests for cattle grazing, and the ensuing production and disposal of wastes (greenhouse gasses and the use of metals, plastics, and paper for infant formula packaging) are prominent features of the manufacture, distribution, and use of commercial infant and baby foods. In contrast, the production and consumption of breastmilk is an environmentally friendly act.

Whose responsibility is it to protect the health of individual families and their children?

As with other public health problems such as epidemics and infectious diseases, it is a government's responsibility to protect the health of families and their children, and not the responsibility of the individual alone. Communities can mobilize to ensure that governments regulate the industries that pollute, and do not compromise the health of their citizens for the interests of business and industry. Successful interventions to reduce pollution occur at the community, national and global levels, when citizens concerned with women's health, children's health and environmental health and justice band together and work collaboratively to take action against the polluters. As consumers, we can change our buying habits and lifestyle choices, and choose not to use or buy products whose production or waste disposal may further pollute the environment.

Who is to blame for this situation?

The blame for this chain of contamination which produces chemical body burdens in us all must be placed on the sources of contamination – the chemical industries responsible and the governments who fail to regulate them or who fail to enforce and monitor protective laws and regulations.

Can media attempts to alert the public to the dangers of contamination influence breastfeeding decisions of mothers?

Media campaigns that insensitively headline stories about contaminated breastmilk in order to draw attention to pollution may discourage breastfeeding. Such campaigns are easily exploited by the commercial baby milk industry who profit at the expense of the health of mothers and children. Breastfeeding is a sensitive process and can be easily disrupted by undermining the mother's confidence in her ability to provide the best food for her infant. Breastfeeding, a human right of all women, cannot be reduced to a risk-benefit equation. Every mother is entitled to up-to-date and accurate information, on the basis of which she makes decisions about feeding her child. She must not be targeted with sensationalized messages about environmental contamination that undermine her confidence in breastfeeding. Instead she should have access to correct, objective, up-to-date information on the full range of issues surrounding infant feeding.

In the context of an alarmist media, how can the practice of breastfeeding be protected?

We must act to ensure that breastfeeding is protected by speaking out about the issue of chemical contamination of all human bodies, male and female, in our communities. As breastfeeding advocates we must continue to be proactive about the superiority of breastmilk, be ready to counter sensationalist messages about "contaminated breastmilk", and reassure mothers about the quality of their breastmilk with advice when necessary about personal choices to reduce risks (advice such as avoiding smoke, not eating fish from polluted sources, etc). Educational and advocacy efforts to promote a toxic-free future for our children should recognize and encourage collective action aimed at reducing chemical contamination and developing the strongest possible pollution prevention laws. We need to work together to ensure that media and the general public understand that the presence of these residues in breastmilk means that toxic chemicals have taken up residence in our bodies and our communities.

What can governments and international organizations do to reduce environmental pollution?

Governments have to be sensitized to the importance of the issue and urged to act in the best interests of children. Some countries have taken positive steps. In Europe, strong governmental programs to eliminate persistent organic pollutants like DDT, dieldrin, PCBs and dioxin have resulted in dramatic decreases of these residues in breastmilk. As a result of controls, Sweden has seen a decline in breastmilk PBDE levels. In the United States, bans on lead in gasoline and smoking in public places have resulted in dramatic decreases in the levels of these dangerous substances or their by-products in the blood of young children. In Canada, several local governments have banned the use of pesticides for cosmetic use on lawns.

These public health achievements show that reductions in the production, use and disposal
of toxic chemicals along with the destruction of toxic chemical stockpiles and reservoirs, can all decrease the body burden of noxious materials in our children and in us. Regulatory frameworks by governments and international organizations are important to minimize and eliminate exposure to harmful contaminants.

International Labour Organization (ILO) Conventions, especially Convention No: 184 on Health and Safety in Agriculture have been particularly helpful. The United Nations Stockholm Convention on Persistent Organic Pollutants (POPs) needs to be ratified by 50 countries before it enters into force. These conventions must be implemented nationally. The Stockholm Convention calls for national bans on incineration. In addition, there are local and national efforts to restrict the use of pesticides and to ban the sale of mercurycontaining products. All of these efforts deserve our energetic and sustained support. Breastmilk is the most ecologically sound and complete first food available to infants. It is the foundation of food security for all children in the first six months of life, and is one of the world's most valuable renewable natural resources. Breastfeeding is a basic human right of every mother, and is essential to fulfill every child's human right to adequate food and to the highest attainable standard of mental and physical health.

There are many women's groups, environmental groups, health activists and breastfeeding advocacy groups who are working to create healthier environments. (See the websites below for the organizations working on this issue.) You can pledge to work with them towards the day when our infants are born free of toxic contamination and our children grow and develop in the healthiest possible world.

The World Alliance for Breastfeeding Action (WABA) is a global alliance of individuals, networks and organisations that protect, promote and support breastfeeding based on the Innocenti Declaration and the WHO/UNICEF Global Strategy on Infant and Young Child Feeding. WABA is in consultative status with UNICEF.

Its core partners are International Baby Food Action Network (IBFAN), La Leche League International (LLLI), International Lactation Consultant Association (ILCA) and Wellstart International. For more information, contact: WABA, P.O.Box 1200, Penang 10850, Malaysia. Fax: 604-6572 655 Email: secr@waba.po.my Website: <www.waba.org.my>.

17 October 2003

This FAQ Sheet emerged out of the combined efforts of breastfeeding and environmental health and justicegroups in addressing breastfeeding in a contaminated environment. These allies seek to understand the issue from both the environmental health and justice and breastfeeding perspectives, share experiences and develop communication strategies to educate the general public, health workers, policy makers and the media. It is based on the recognition that breastfeeding promotion should take place alongside efforts to eliminate toxic chemicals from the environment. The WABA Breastfeeding and Environment Working Group and the WABA Secretariat coordinated the collaborative process and preparation of the document for publication.

This FAQ Sheet, "Towards Healthy Environments for Children: Frequently Asked Questions About Breastfeeding in a Contaminated Environment," was prepared by Penny van Esterik (York University, Toronto), author of "Risks, Rights and Regulation: Communicating about Risks and Infant Feeding" and member of WABA Breastfeeding and Environment Working Group with the assistance of: Baby Milk Action, UK; Commonweal/IPEN Working Group on Community Monitoring, USA; IBFAN-GIFA, Switzerland; Initiativ Liewensufank, Luxembourg; INFACT, Canada; La Leche League International, USA; National Networks on Environments and Women's Health, Canada, and WABA Secretariat, Malaysia.

References

Berlin, C. and S. Kacew. 1997. "Environmental Chemicals in Human Milk." In: *Environmental Toxicology and Pharmacology of Human Development.* S. Kacew and G. Lambert, eds. Washington: Taylor and Francis.

Boersma, E. and C. Lanting. 2000. Environmental Exposure to Polychlorinated Biphenyls (PCBs) and Dioxins. *Adv Exp Med Biol* 478: 271-87.

Carson, Rachael. 1987. *Silent Spring.* Houghton Mifflin Company: New York University

Chaudhuri, N. 1998. Child Health, Poverty and the Environment: The Canadian Context. *Canadian Journal of Public Health* 89 (1): S26-S30.

Colborn, T., D. Dumanoski, and J. Myers. 1996. *Our Stolen Future.* New York: Plume.

Dewailly, Eric, P. Ayotte, S. Bruneau, S. Gingras, M. Belles-Isles, and R. Roy. 2000. Susceptibility to Infections and Immune Status in Inuit Infants Exposed to Organochlorines. *Environmental Health Perspectives* 108 (3): 205-211.

Frank, J. and J. Newman. 1993. Breastfeeding in a Polluted World: Uncertain Risks, Clear Benefits, *Canadian Medical Association Journal* 149 (1): 33-37.

Goldman, L., R. Newbold and S. Swan. 2001. Exposure to Soy-Based Formula in Infancy? *JAMA* 286 (19).

Huisman, M. et al. 1995. Neurological Condition in 18-month-old Children Perinatally Exposed to Polychlorinated Biphenyls and Dioxins. *Early Human Development* 43: 165-176.

Infante-Rivard, C. and D. Sinnett. 1999. Preconceptual Paternal Exposure to Pesticides and Increased Risk of Childhood Leukemia. *Lancet* 354: 1819.

Jensen, A. and S. Slorach. 1991. *Chemical Contaminants in Human Milk*. Boca Raton: CRC Press, Inc.

Lawrence, Ruth and Linda R. Friedman. 1995. "Contaminants in Milk" In: *Handbook of Milk Composition*. Robert G. Jensen, ed. New York: Academic Press.

Nelson, B. K. et al. 1996. Review of Experimental Male-mediated Behavioral and Neurochemical Disorders. *Neurotoxicol Teratol* 18 (6): 611-16.

Radford, A. 1992. The Ecological Impact of Bottle-Feeding. *Breastfeeding Review* 2 (1): 204-208.

Rogan, W. 1996. Pollutants in Breast Milk. *Archives of Pediatric and Adolescent Medicine* 150 (9): 981-990.

Steingraber, Sandra. 2001. *Having Faith: An Ecologist's Journey to Motherhood*. Cambridge, Massachusetts: Perseus Publishing.

Van Acker et al. 2001. Outbreak of necrotizing enterocolitis associated with *Enterobacter sakazakii* in powdered milk formula. *J Clin. Microbiol* 39:293-97.

Van Esterik, Penny. 2002. *Risks, Rights and Regulation: Communicating about Risk and Infant Feeding*. WABA: Penang; NNEWH, York University.

Walker, M. 1998. *Summary of the Hazards of Infant Formula, Part 2*. International Lactation Consultants Association: Raleigh, N.C. *Working Together for a Toxic-Free Future*, WABA/IPEN 2002.

Websites

Baby Milk Action
www. babymilkaction.org

Chemical Reaction
www.chemicalreaction.org

International Baby Food Action Network
www.ibfan.org

International Lactation Consultant Association
www.ilca.org

International POPs Elimination Network
www.ipen.org

La Leche League International
www.lalecheleague.org

National Network on Environments and Women's Health
www.yorku.ca/nnewh/

World Alliance for Breastfeeding Action
www.waba.org.my

Women's Health Care Work with Children with Cancer

JUANNE NANCARROW CLARKE, DEPARTMENT OF SOCIOLOGY, WILFRED LAURIER UNIVERSITY
PAULA C. FLETCHER, DEPARTMENT OF KINESIOLOGY AND PHYSICAL EDUCATION, WILFRED LAURIER UNIVERSITY
MARGARET SCHNEIDER, DEPARTMENT OF KINESIOLOGY AND PHYSICAL EDUCATION, WILFRED LAURIER UNIVERSITY

The data for this study was collected through ten focus groups with mothers of children with cancer, conducted across Ontario and Quebec. More specifically, one focus group was conducted in each of the following cities: Barrie, Windsor, Ottawa, Sudbury, and London. Three focus groups were conducted in Quebec and two were conducted in Kitchener-Waterloo, Ontario. These focus groups started in February 2001, and continued through to October of 2001. The total number of participants in these focus groups was 49, and on average, five women participated in each focus group. The length of these focus groups varied from one to three hours.

Description of the Mothers

The mothers who participated in this study ranged in age from 29 to 50 years of age, with a mean age of 39.19 years. Twenty-five percent of these women had completed college, CEGEP, or nursing school, and 22% had completed a university degree. Only 3.4% of these women had not completed primary or secondary school, whereas a comparatively larger number (10%) had completed a post-graduate degree. When questioned about their ethnic or cultural identity, 24% identified themselves as English, and 37% identified themselves as Canadian. Despite the overwhelming number of women in both of these categories, women of many different ethnic backgrounds were involved in this study. Some of the other nationalities represented included women of French Canadian (5.1%), Scottish (3.4%), and Italian Canadian (3.4%) descent. Others identified with being African, Polish, East Indian, and North American Native, to name but a few. In total, 17 different ethnic or cultural identities were represented.

Description of their Children with Cancer

The children ranged in age from 14 months to twenty-one years of age, with a mean age of nine years. The mean age at diagnosis for these children was six years old. The majority (53%) of these children had been diagnosed with Acute Lymphoblastic Leukemia (ALL), while another 3% had a form of Leukemia that was unspecified by the parent. Neuroblastoma was the next most frequent type of childhood cancer reported, affecting 9% of these children. Hodgkin's Lymphoma, Ewing's Sarcoma, Rhabdomyosarcoma, Wilm's Tumour, and Retinoblastoma each affected five percent of these children, while approximately 9% were affected by other miscellaneous forms of cancer. The length of treatment these children received ranged from 3.5 months to 101 months, with a mean of 29 months. Those children who had had fewer months of treatment tended to be those children who had recently been diagnosed and were just beginning their treatment regimen. When questioned about the relative length of time these children spent in the hospital as compared to being cared for in the home over the course of their illness, the average length of time was 27 months and 45 months, respectively.

The specific treatment received by almost all of the children in this study was chemotherapy (95%). The next most common treatments included surgery (58%) and radiation (46%). All three were prescribed by a doctor, in each particular case. Only 19% of the children received treatments that were complementary or alternative in nature, of which 30% had been prescribed by a doctor. Some of the complementary treatments used included herbalism, acupuncture, naturopathy, and holistic energy healing, to name but a few. Among the other treatments used were physiotherapy and massage therapies.

Access to Treatment

The majority of these women (73%) lived in relatively large cities ranging from 50,000 to one million or more inhabitants. Only nine percent lived in towns with fewer than 5,000 people. With this said, most participants had to travel to receive treatment. The average distance to the nearest treatment centre was 165 kilometres. Twenty-seven percent of the sample received additional treatment at a satellite centre, which was often closer to their home than traveling the full distance to the primary treatment centre. Most of these women (92%) drove their own children to treatments using their personal cars, rarely requiring assistance from others to access treatment. Nine percent of the mothers relied on other family members, public transit, or Canadian Cancer Society (CCS) volunteer drivers. Women who lived in rural communities tended to also rely on medical flights, rental cars, and medical taxis. Of those women who used satellite treatment centres, all reported using their own cars to get to treatment and few reported the use of other means to get to these treatment centres.

Family Lives

The majority of these women (90%) were married or living with an intimate partner, while five percent were separated or divorced. Only one mother in this study had never been married, and one mother was a widow. Seven percent of the sample lived as single parents, while 92% lived with a partner. All of the women in this sample had children, with a range from one to four per household, and a mean of 1.88 or approximately two children per family. Seventy-six percent of these women reported English to be the language spoken most often at home, while ten percent reported speaking French, seven percent reported being bilingual, and three percent reported speaking Spanish. In terms of household composition, only five percent lived with other family members. With regards to household income, the majority (70%) had an income greater than $40,000 per year, with 40% earning between $40,000 and $79,999, and 31% earning between $80,000 and $100,000 or more.

Work Lives

With regards to their work lives, 60% of these women reported that they had been working at a job when their child was diagnosed with cancer. Twenty percent were working in the home at the time, seven percent were looking for work, and five percent were self-employed or on maternity leave. When questioned about what their usual occupation was, 17% reported that they held some type of managerial position. Other commonly cited occupations included homemaking (17%), administrative assistance (15%), healthcare professions, including nurses and physiotherapists (10%), and jobs in the area of business (9%). These women also reported that their husbands occupied business positions (17%), labourer positions (15%), managerial positions (10%), sales agent positions (9%), or were self-employed (9%). Although 42% of the women stopped working entirely once their child was diagnosed, only 2% of their spouses did so. Rather, 49% of their spouses reported that their work life did not change at all.

Women's Health Care Work With Children With Cancer

by Juanne Clarke, Paula C. Fletcher and Margaret Schneider

INTRODUCTION

Each year an estimated 1,300 to 1,400 children are diagnosed with various childhood cancers, joining the 8 to 10,000 children that are currently coping with cancer and its detrimental effects. With respect to childhood cancer, considerable research has been completed on the adjustment and coping of parents (see Grootenhuis and Last, 1995 for a review of the literature which includes 83 research articles published on this topic). The impact of socio-psychological variables such as social support, coping, and adjustment has been investigated. Much less is known about the home health care challenges faced by mothers, or the impact these have on the health of mothers. Problems and proposed solutions from the point of view of the mothers has not been studied. As such, this research focuses on women's health care work in the home and in liaison with hospitals and clinics, and in the hospitals, in the situation where a child has cancer.

OBJECTIVE

Specifically, the objective of this research is to describe the work that mothers complete when their children have cancer, and to explore the self-perceived impacts of this "home" health care work on the mothers.

METHODOLOGY

Participants

Six focus groups were conducted with mothers from Ontario and Quebec whose children had been diagnosed with cancer during the previous five year period. On average, each focus group had approximately five mothers who participated.

Procedure

The focus groups ranged in length from 1-3 hours, and followed an unstructured format where the women were asked to comment on their experiences of the home health care work they completed on behalf of their children.

Data Analysis

The focus group audiotapes were transcribed verbatim. These transcripts were then analysed using Patton's method of phenomenological analysis and Glaser and Strauss' (1967) constant comparative method, following which the data were then coded according to the emerging themes.

FINDINGS

The women in these focus groups described the home health care tasks they performed for their children on a daily basis, and the effect of caregiving on their overall well-being. Among the emerging task-related themes were illness management roles and emotion work. In response to these roles, one of the methods these women used to cope was to organise their lives by establishing boundaries and setting limits.

Illness Management Roles

One of the roles these women described was an illness management role. It involved acting as an advocate for their child, ensuring that their child's medical needs were met by the staff and speaking out when their needs were not met.

Quote: "Something that you realise very quick when your kids are sick is that you have to be there. You may have to step on a few toes. I was one that did....I stood up for him a lot."

As part of their illness management role, they also described the necessity to perform the tasks of a 'makeshift nurse'. This included administering medications and monitoring all aspects of their child's treatment, which added further tasks to their already burgeoning workload.

Quote: "I've had to learn. Before C. got sick, I was the least medically capable person. I didn't like to deal with it.... I had to learn how to give injections. I had to learn how to use the CAD pump. In the middle of the night one night, the VON came and we programmed the pump incorrectly...so I was on the phone, almost 3 hours away talking to the nurse saying, 'Are you comfortable with changing the bag?' And I said, 'That doesn't enter into it. Tell me how to do it'....I didn't think I needed to know how to give an exact medication....And now it's like, 'You want to do the injection?' 'Sure, I [can] do that'."

Emotion Work

Dealing with the medical system and its staff was part of the emotion work these women engaged in. In particular, they had to deal with often feeling misunderstood by the medical staff and wanting a level of support that was not available to them.

Quote: "When you are on treatment there is a safety zone. When you are off then you wonder is it going to come back? There is no way of knowing until they are off the treatment and start living without the medicine, to see what the body actually does. Those few months are scary. I tried to explain that to certain people—to the nurses, to the doctors.... I felt that I was given a kind of false hope at the time. I thought, there needs to be some kind of emotional something that can help you live with the fear all the time."

As part of their emotion work these women also described the necessity of dealing with their family's responses to the child's illness. This too, was perceived to be a difficult task.

Quote: "It's not just the kid that just has cancer, it's your other children, your husband, your extended family, you know, dealing with all of that. How do we deal with that? How do you deal with that? How do we deal with the other child that has other disabilities or the healthy child, supposedly? All problems [suddenly] become magnified. If you had a little conflict going on before, now it becomes—the molehill is now the Alps!"

Establishing Boundaries

In dealing with the impact of the emotion work and in response to the fatigue and frustrations many of these women experienced, some of them resorted to organising their lives and establishing boundaries. One way in which this was achieved was through scheduling and ensuring that family visits did not interfere with the child's medical treatment

Quote: "[My Mom] would say, 'Why can't I come to the hospital at this time?', and I would say, 'You can't because of this schedule and these are the hours', and she would say, 'Well that doesn't suit me best', and I would say, 'I am sorry. This is the time, and I have to go by the hospital hours. If that doesn't suit you that is okay, but this is the best time that suits us.' She didn't like it."

DISCUSSION

It is crucial that medical professionals who deal with families on a daily basis recognize the many roles of parents of a child with cancer, and attempt to support them in their caregiving journey. Staff in-services, where this information is discussed, would be well-warranted to achieve this desired end result.

Nineteen percent did, however, change the number of hours they spent at work following their child's diagnosis, and an additional 15% changed the nature of their work. Twenty percent of the mothers reported reducing the number of hours they spent at work upon their child's diagnosis, and 22% had not been working prior to the diagnosis.

Theories on Cancer Causation

When questioned about perceived cancer causation, none of these women reported having worked around or near any cancer causing substances. However, 37% stated that they did not know whether or not they had. In contrast, 7% reported living near a cancer causing substance, with 39% reporting that they did not know whether or not they did. The types of substances reported included hydro-electrical wires and towers (33%), mines and chimneys (25%), and pesticides applied to nearby farmer's fields (17%).

Conclusion

Overall, this sample of mothers differed in various aspects of their experiences of childhood cancer. Whether it was due to a varied family composition or length of active treatment, each of these women had a slightly different perspective of the impact of this illness, and this perception is likely influenced by their particular experiences and specific sociodemographic characteristics.

Reference List

Avison, W.R., Noh, S., & Speechley, K. (1991). Parents as caregivers: Caring for children with health problems. *Advances in Medical Psychology, 2*, 65-94.

Barakat, L., & Kazak, A. (1999). Family issues. In R. T. Brown (Ed.), *Cognitive aspects of chronic illness in children.* (pp. 333-354). New York, NY: The Guilford Press.

Barakat, L., Kazak, A., Gallagher, P., Meeske, K., & Stuber, M. (2000). Posttraumatic stress symptoms and stressful life events predict the long-term adjustment of survivors of childhood cancer and their mothers. *Journal of Clinical Psychology in Medical Settings, 7*(4), 189-196.

Barakat, L.P., Kazak, A.E., Meadows, A.T., Casey, R., Meeske, K., & Stuber, M.L. (1997). Families surviving childhood cancer: A comparison of posttraumatic stress symptoms with families of healthy children. *Journal of Pediatric Psychology, 22*(6), 843-859.

Barbarin, O.A. (1983). Coping with ecological transitions by black families: A psychosocial model. *Journal of Community Psychology, 11*, 308-322.

Barbarin, O.A., & Chesler, M.A. (1984). Coping as interpersonal strategy: Families with childhood cancer. *Family Systems Medicine, 2*(3), 279-289.

Barbarin, O.A., & Chesler, M.A. (1986). The medical context of parental coping with childhood cancer. *American Journal of Community Psychology, 14*(2), 221-235.

Barnhart, L.L., Fitzpatrick, V.D., Sidell, N.L., Adams, M.J., & Gomez, S.J. (1994). Perception of family need in pediatric oncology. *Child and Adolescent Social Work Journal, 11*(2), 137-148.

Bearison, D.J., Sadow, A.J., Granowetter, L., & Winkel, G. (1993). Patients' and parents' causal attributions for childhood cancer. *Journal of Psychosocial Oncology, 11*(3), 47-61.

Birenbaum, L.K. (1990). Family coping with childhood cancer. *The Hospice Journal, 6*(3), 17-33.

Chesler, M.A. (1991). Mobilizing consumer activism in health care: The role of self-help groups. *Research in Social Movements, Conflicts, and Change, 13*, 275-305.

Chesney, B.K., & Chesler, M.A. (1996). Listening to their voices: Understanding the "meaning" of parental coping with childhood cancer. Applied Behavioral Science Review, 4(2), 177-190.

Clegg, N.J. (1997). The relationship between parents' perceptions of coping, quality of family relationships, and selected sociodemographic and illness-related variables and family adaptation in families of children diagnosed with cancer. Dissertation Abstracts International, B: The Sciences and Engineering, 58(1-B), 0134.

Cook, J.A. (1983). The social construction of gender in the parenting of dying children. North Central Sociological Association.

Cornman, B.J. (1989). Impact of childhood cancer on the family. Dissertation Abstracts International, 49(7-A), 1976.

Darbasie, D. (2000). Psychological stress and social support networks: An analysis of mothers and fathers of childhood cancer survivors. Dissertation Abstracts International, B: The Sciences and Engineering, 60(7-B), 3559.

de Vilaro, M. (1985). Coping strategies and adaptation to childhood cancer of Puerto Rican families. Dissertation Abstracts International, 45(12-B, Pt. 1), 3773-3774.

Desmond, H.A. (1978). The psychological impact of childhood cancer on the family. Dissertation Abstracts International, 38(10-B), 5008.

Dixon-Woods, M., Findlay, M., Young, B., Cox, H., & Heney, D. (2001). Parents' accounts of obtaining a diagnosis of childhood cancer. Lancet, 357(9257), 670-674.

Dockerty, J., Williams, S., McGee, R., & Skegg, D. (2000). Impact of childhood cancer on the mental health of parents. Medicine in Pediatric Oncology, 35(5), 475-483.

Dolgin, M.J., & Phipps, S. (1996). Reciprocal influences in family adjustment to childhood cancer. In L. Baider & C. L. Cooper (Eds.), Cancer and the family. (pp. 73-92). NY: John Wiley & Sons.

Dufour, D.F. (1989). Home or hospital care for the child with end-stage cancer: Effects on the family. Issues in Comprehensive Pediatric Nursing, 12(5), 371-383.

Eiser, C., Havermans, T., & Eiser, J.R. (1995). Parents' attributions about childhood cancer: Implications for relationships with medical staff. Child: Care, Health, and Development, 21(1), 31-42.

Eiser, C. (1994). Making sense of chronic disease: The Eleventh Jack Tizard Memorial Lecture. The Journal of Child Psychology and Psychiatry and Allied Disciplines, 35, 1373-1389.

Eiser, C., & Eiser, R. (2000). Social comparisons and quality of life among survivors of childhood cancer and their mothers. Psychology and Health, 15(3), 435-450.

Friedman, M.M. (1985). Family stress and coping among anglo and latino families with childhood cancer. Dissertation Abstracts International, 46(2-A), 528.

Gilliss, C.L. (1997). Measuring parental grief after childhood cancer: Potential use of the SCL-90R. Death Studies, 21, 277-287.

Greenberg, H., & Meadows, A. (1991). Psychosocial impact of cancer survival on school-age children and their parents. Journal of Psychosocial Oncology, 9(4), 43-56.

Grootenhuis, M.A., Last, B.F., De Graaf-Nijkerk, J.H., & Van Der Wel, M. (1996). Secondary control strategies used by parents of children with cancer. Psycho-Oncology, 5(2), 91-102.

Hall, M., & Baum, A. (1995). Intrusive thoughts as determinants of distress in parents of children with cancer. Journal of Applied Social Psychology, 25(14), 1215-1230.

Hoekstra-Weebers, J., Jaspers, J., & Kamps, W. (1999). Risk factors for psychological maladjustment of parents of children with cancer. Journal of the American Academy of Child and Adolescent Psychiatry, 38(12), 1526-1535.

Hoekstra-Weebers, J.E.H.M., Jaspers, J.P.C., Kamps, W., & Klip, E. (1998). Marital dissatisfaction, psychological distress, and the coping of parents of pediatric cancer patients. *Journal of Marriage and the Family, 60*(4), 1012-1021.

Horwitz, W.A., & Kazak, A.E. (1990). Family adaptation to childhood cancer: Sibling and family systems. *Journal of Clinical Child Psychology, 19*(3), 221-228.

Huber, J.R. (1990). Mothers' adaptation to childhood cancer: An analysis of family process stressors, family system resources, parental coping patterns, and parental adaptation among mothers of children with cancer. *Dissertation Abstracts International, A: The Humanities and Social Sciences, 51*(5), 1792-A.

Hughes, P.M., & Lieberman, S. (1990). Troubled parents: Vulnerability and stress in childhood cancer. British *Journal of Medical Psychology, 63*, 53-64.

Katz, E.R., & Jay, S.M. (1984). Psychological aspects of cancer in children, adolescents, and their families. *Clinical Psychology Review, 4*(5), 525-542.

Kazak, A., Stuber, M., & Barakat, L. (1998). Predicting posttraumatic stress symptoms in mothers and fathers of survivors of childhood cancers. *Journal of the American Academy of Child and Adolescent Psychiatry, 37*(8), 823-831.

Kazak, A.E., Barakat, L.P., Meeske, K., Christakis, D., Meadows, A.T., Penati, B., & Stuber, M. (1997). Posttraumatic stress, family functioning, and social support in survivors of childhood leukemia and their mothers and fathers. *Journal of Consulting and Clinical Psychology, 65*(1), 120-129.

Kazak, A.E., Christakis, D., Alderfer, M., & Coiro, M.J. (1994). Young adolescent cancer survivors and their parents: Adjustment, learning problems, and gender. *Journal of Family Psychology, 8*(1), 74-84.

Kazak, A.E., & Christakis, D.A. (1996). The intense stress of childhood cancer: A systems perspective. In C. R. Pfeffer (Ed.), *Severe stress and mental distrubance in children.* (pp. 277-305). Washington, DC: American Psychiatric Press.

Kazak, A.E., & Meadows, A.T. (1989). Families of young adolescents who have survived cancer: Social-emotional adjustment, adaptability, and social support. *Journal of Pediatric Psychology, 14*(2), 175-191.

LaMontagne, Wells, Hepworth, Johnson, & Manes. (1999). *Journal of Pediatric Oncology Nursing, 16*(1), 3-12.

Leavitt, M., Martinson, I., Liu, C., Armstrong, V., Hornberger, L., Zhang, J., & Han, X. (1999). Comparison of Chinese and Caucasian families caregiving to children with cancer at home: Part II. *Journal of Pediatric Nursing, 14*(2), 110-122.

Leventhal-Belfer, L., Bakker, A.M., & Russo, C.L. (1993). Parents of childhood cancer survivors: A descriptive look at their concerns and needs. *Journal of Psychosocial Oncology, 11*(2), 19-41.

Levi, Marsick, Drotar, & Kodish. (2000). *Journal of Pediatric Hematology Oncology, 22*(1), 3-12.

Lozowski, S., Chesler, M.A., & Chesney, B.K. (1993). Parental intervention in the medical care of children with cancer. *Journal of Psychosocial Oncology, 11*(3), 63-88.

Macaskill, A., & Monach, J.H. (1990). Coping with childhood cancer: The case for long-term counselling help for patients and their families. *British Journal of Guidance and Counselling, 18*(1), 13-27.

Majidi-Ahi, S. (1990). Childhood cancer: Coping strategies used by children and their mothers. *Dissertation Abstracts International, 50*(7-B), 3166-3167.

Manne, S., Du Hamel, K., Gallelli, K., Sorgen, K., & Redd, W. (1998). Posttraumatic stress disorder among mothers of pediatric cancer survivors: Diagnosis, comorbidity, and utility of the PTSD Checklist as a screening instrument. *Journal of Pediatric Psychology, 23*(6), 357-366.

Martinson, I., Leavitt, M., Liu, C., Armstrong, V., Hornberger, L., Zhang, J., & Han, X. (1999). Comparison of Chinese and Caucasian families caregiving to children with cancer at home: Part I.

Journal of Pediatric Nursing, 14(2), 99-109.

Martinson, I.M., & Cohen, M.H. (1988). Themes from a longitudinal study of family reaction to childhood cancer. *Journal of Psychosocial Oncology, 6*(3/4), 81-98.

Martinson, I.M., McClowry, S.G., Davies, B., & Kuhlenkamp, E.J. (1994). Changes over time: A study of family bereavement following childhood cancer. *Journal of Palliative Care, 10*(1), 19-25.

Maury, J.L. (1983). Patterns of coping with the stages of cancer: The child-patient and his/her family. *Dissertation Abstracts International, 43*(9-A), 3116.

McClowry, S.G., Davies, E.B., May, K.A., Kulenkamp, E.J., & Martinson, I.M. (1987). The empty space phenomenon: The process of grief in the bereaved family. *Death Studies, 11,* 361-374.

Niles, M. (1996). Post-traumatic stress in response to childhood cancer: An examination of child/adolescent cancer survivors and their parents. *Dissertation Abstracts International, B: The Sciences and Engineering, 56*(9-B), 5179.

Noll, R.B., Gartstein, M.A., Hawkins, A., Vannatta, K., Hobart Davies, W., & Bukowski, W.M. (1995). Comparing parental distress for families with children who have cancer and matched comparison families without children with cancer. *Family Systems Medicine, 13* (1), 11-27.

Noojin, A., Causey, D., Gros, B., Bertolone, S., & Carter, B. (1999). The influence of maternal stress resistance and family relationships on depression in children with cancer. *Journal of Psychosocial Oncology, 17*(2), 79-97.

O'Neil, J.A. (1996). Naming the silences: A hermeneutic phenomenology of the dimensions of parental decision-making in pediatric oncology. *Dissertation Abstracts International, B: The Sciences and Engineering, 56*(12-B), 6673.

Ogg, M.G. (1998). The effects of pediatric cancer on fathers during the diagnostic and initial treatment phases. *Dissertation Abstracts International, B: The Sciences and Engineering, 58*(9-B), 5135.

Overholser, J.C., & Fritz, G.K. (1990). The impact of childhood cancer on the family. *Journal of Psychosocial Oncology, 8*(4), 71-85.

Pellino-Benner, M.E. (1989). Childhood cancer as a family disease: A case study of the belief systems developed in relation to family dynamics. *Dissertation Abstracts International, 50*(5-B), 2162.

Reay, D., Bignold, S., Ball, S., & Cribb, A. (1998). "He just had a different way of showing it": Gender dynamics in families coping with childhood cancer. *Journal of Gender Studies, 7*(1), 39-52.

Ross, J.W. (1980). Childhood cancer: The parents, the patients, the professionals. *Issues in Comprehensive Pediatric Nursing, 4*(1), 7-16.

Ross, J.W. (1982). The role of the social worker with long term survivors of childhood cancer and their families. *Social Work in Health Care, 7*(4), 1-13.

Sawyer, M., Streiner, D., Antoniou, G., Toogood, I., & Rice, M. (1998). Influence of parental and family adjustment on the later psychological adjustment of children treated for cancer. *Journal of the American Academy of Child and Adolescent Psychiatry, 37*(8), 815-822.

Sawyer, M., Antoniou, G., Toogood, I., & Rice, M. (1997). Childhood cancer: A two-year prospective study of the psychological adjustment of children and parents. *Journal of the American Academy of Child and Adolescent Psychiatry, 36*(12), 1736-1743.

Sawyer, M., Antoniou, G., Toogood, I., Rice, M., & Baghurst, P. (2000). Childhood cancer: A 4-year prospective study of the psychological adjustment of children and parents. *Journal of Pediatric Hematology Oncology, 22*(3), 214-220.

Schaefer, D.S. (1983). Issues related to psychosocial intervention with Hispanic families in a pediatric cancer setting. *Journal of Psychosocial Oncology, 1*(4), 39-46.

Shapiro, J. (1983). Family reactions and coping strategies in response to the physically ill or handicapped child: A review. *Social Science and Medicine, 17*(14), 913-931.

Shields, G., Schondel, C., Barnhart, L., & Fitzpatrick, V. (1995). Social work in pediatric oncology: A family needs assessment. *Social Work in Health Care, 21*(1), 39-54.

Sourkes, B. (1977). Facilitating family coping with childhood cancer. *Journal of Pediatric Psychology, 2*(2), 65-67.

Speechley, K.N. (1987). Surviving childhood cancer: The psychosocial impact on parents. *Dissertation Abstracts International, 48*(6-B), 1637-1638.

Speechley, K.N., & Noh, S. (1992). Surviving childhood cancer, social support, and parents' psychological adjustment. *Journal of Pediatric Psychology, 17*(1), 15-31.

Spilka, B., Zwartjes, W., & Zwartjes, G.M. (1991). The role of religion in coping with childhood cancer. *Pastoral Psychology, 39*(5), 295-304.

Spinetta, J.J., Murphy, J.L., Vik, P.J., & Day, J. (1988). Long-term adjustment in families of children with cancer. *Journal of Psychosocial Oncology—Special Issue: Clinical research issues in psychosocial oncology, 6*(3/4), 179-191.

Stuber, M.L. (1996). Psychiatric sequelae in seriously ill children and their families. *Psychiatric Clinics of North America, 19*(3), 481-493.

Van Dongen-Melman, J.E.W.M., Pruyn, J.F.A., De Groot, A., Koot, H.M., Hahlen, K., & Verhulst, F.C. (1995). Late psychosocial consequences for parents of children who survived cancer. *Journal of Pediatric Psychology, 20*(5), 567-586.

Williams, H.A. (1995). There are no free gifts! Social support and the need for reciprocity. *Human Organization, 54*(4), 401-409.

The Impacts of Policy on the Health and Well-being of Women Raising Children with Disabilities

CANADIAN ASSOCIATION FOR COMMUNITY LIVING

It is our belief that our sons and daughters are not seen as individuals or people as is their right under the Charter of Rights and Freedoms. If the policies and regulations intended to support our children do not value them, they do not value us. (Mother raising a child with a disability)

In October 2000, a round table was held with mothers raising children with disabilities as key informants. The purpose of the roundtable was to explore the impacts of policy on women's health and well-being related to raising children with disabilities. The themes explored were how the different roles taken on by the women raising children with disabilities impact on their personal health and well-being and to investigate the policies that affect the physical and mental health of women; perspectives on the responsiveness of service providers and the impact on women's health and well-being; and the status of informal community support their impact on women's health status. The round table held in Edmonton, Alberta took place in conjunction with the 6th International Congress on the Inclusion of Children with Disabilities and the Canadian Association for Community Living Family Conference.

It is apparent that the current state of affairs for some women who are raising children with disabilities has a significant impact on their own health and well-being, as well as on their social and economic opportunities and sense of social security. Mothers raising children with disabilities are clear that the negative impacts on their own health and well-being are a direct result of current policy and the translation in delivery of programs and service, not the direct care of their child per se.

CONSIDERING

That the majority of policies, programs and treatment by professionals force these women as mothers and as primary caregivers to constantly portray their child in a negative and deficit-based manner, continuously justify their request for supports and jump through endless hoops. Bureaucratic processes that insist that parents (usually the mothers) describe their children in a devaluing manner perpetuate mothers' feelings of betrayal of their own child. Parents are required to use intrusive and degrading language to obtain the necessary services and supports. Yet at the same time these very women have become peripheral to the process that determines the supports and services.

That the status of current policy and supports may subject a number of these women to make choices that subject their children to an environment that puts them at risk and may have the potential of giving up their child with a disability.

That mothers raising children with disabilities are contributors of "unpaid" work. They are primarily assuming multiple roles not only as a mother, but as caregiver, advocate, planner, coordinator, trainer, nurse, educator, etc. They spend an extraordinary amount of time in meetings with professionals, especially in the health, social services and education sectors. Although these women go "beyond the limits" they are spending enormous time and energy as a direct result of current policy and are doing jobs previously done by a paid workforce. They also face society's expectations of caregiving and nurturing responsibilities.

That there has been a shift to the privatization of responsibility to families, and that responsibility is primarily being born by women who have little or no control over their child or their own life. They have little control over who provides them with support, how much support they receive and the manner in which support is provided to them.

That frequently women are isolated within their communities, removed from extended family, sometimes must be relocated in order to access a more inclusive environment for their child (such as a particular school), and having to leave their family's community and supportive neighbours.

That the current formulation and translation of policy and programs is characterized by a deficit- and label-based model; defining supports and services through classification and restrictive categories of disability and are disability-related as compared to encompassing a family support approach. Presently, many of the programs are redefining disability and in fact are excluding more and more children In addition, most policies are arranged specific to the child with the disability, instead of regarding the child in the context of supports to the family. Children and their families are penalized for any advances or gains made by the child, with the results of a reduction of supports and services.

That the current state of policies undermines equality for mothers raising children with disabilities. Existing policies, programs and services necessitate dependence. These circumstances inhibit women raising children with disabilities in attaining equality because they are positioned as dependent when they receive support. Thus in effect, as mothers work toward their children's independence they are forced to rely on services that create an even greater dependency on a system. This dependency further compromises the equality of these women.

That the participation of women raising children with disabilities in the paid labour force is prohibited, delayed or severely restricted. The lack of family-friendly workplaces, inclusive child care options, inclusive school options, and limited employment opportunities, housing and support options for their adult children, place enormous pressure and economic strain on these women across their children's lifespan.

That inequalities exist in relationships between mothers and providers. There appears to be little acknowledgement or validation of the mother's expertise. They are expected to share painstaking details, yet these women often feel that they are not listened to or respected. Frequently, professionals are insensitive in the manner in which they talk to a mother and how they talk about her child.

That there are a number of types of support for which women may need entitlement that simply do not exist.

That mothers raising children with disabilities find it beneficial to have networking opportunities and support from other mothers who are also raising children with disabilities.

RECOMMENDATIONS

1. That mothers raising children with disabilities be given a place as decision makers at the policy tables.

2. Policy makers pay particular attention to and address circumstances that require women to perform the majority of unpaid work involved in caregiving. We encourage the devising of policies to promote equality for mothers raising children with disabilities that acknowledges their expertise, recognizes and compensates them for their unpaid caregiving activities. Development of entitlements such as caregiver compensation should be deployed.

3. Mechanisms need to be developed to ensure equality for women when accessing services and supports. They must be treated with respect and given equal participation in identifying their child's and family's needs in the context of their lifestyles and relationships.

4. Governments must make a commitment to ensure that there will be no future investments in the institutionalization of children with disabilities and that families will not be forced to give up their child with a disability in order to get support.

5. The establishment of formal support for the implementation and sustainability of family networks and parent-to-parent support.

6. The creation of an alternative model to the deficit/label-based framework for accessing services and supports. It should be based on the premises of celebration, success and build on the strengths of the child and family. The premise for eligibility needs to account for the complexity of these children and their family's lives and the social and economic barriers must be embedded in the policy framework through inclusion of principles such as self-determination.

7. Strategies for reconstruction of policies and programs. The transition to community based care and to a social model of disability needs to be reflected in related policies. An example would be in the reduction in bureaucracy and redesign of programs and processes to ease the application process in accessing services.

8. We urge the construction of family support policies.

9. Implementation of family-friendly work place policies, inclusive education policies and inclusive child care policies to enhance the opportunity for women raising children with disabilities to participate in the paid labour force.

10. Professional development and formalized training of professionals in their curriculum, involving mothers who are/have raised children with disabilities in addition to the provision of current research in this area.

11. Future work needs to explore the "harm" done to women by the prevalence and "forced" devaluing of their children and themselves.

12. An information strategy is needed to raise public awareness, and to provide parents, professionals, and government officials with the information they need to promote the understanding and acceptance of a social model of
disability and family support.

Biotechnology and the New Genetics
What it Means for Women's Health

ANNE ROCHON FORD, WORKING GROUP ON WOMEN AND HEALTH PROTECTION

The Working Group on Women, Health and the New Genetics comprises Canadian academics and community activists concerned with the impact of the new genetics and biotechnology on women's health. The Working Group is committed to principles and practices of feminism, equality and social justice.

The Working Group's current focus is the Canadian Biotechnology Strategy (CBS), a policy document of the federal government that promotes the Canadian biotechnology industry. The Group is concerned about the lack of attention to the implications for women's health in the CBS and on the part of the Canadian biotechnology industry as a whole.

In February 2000, we held a workshop in Toronto at which these issues were discussed. This booklet is loosely based on the presentations and discussions at that workshop. A number of documents of the Working Group, including a community mobilizing tool ("Gender and Genetics: A Feminist Analysis of the Canadian Biotechnology Strategy and Alternative Visions for Community Action") and the proceedings from the workshop ("The Gender of Genetic Futures: The Canadian Biotechnology Strategy, Women and Health"), are available on the CWHN website (www.cwhn.ca).

Genetics and biotechnology are changing so rapidly that a booklet such as this can only represent a snapshot in time. So, while some of the technical information may quickly become outdated, we hope that the discussion will contribute to a critical understanding of the ethical and other substantive issues involved in the development and application of these technologies.

Introduction

The development and growing popularity of biotechnology and new genetics raise fundamental questions about who we are as humans in the twenty-first century. We are at a moment in time when life forms can be patented and our genes can be sold on the commercial market. At the same time as governments are recognizing that social factors such as poverty and violence influence our health, a persistent view that much can be determined by genetics is quickly becoming "normalized" in the public consciousness. While one trend broadens a view of health, the second medicalizes it further.

Despite the importance of these technologies and their relevance to our health, Canadians know relatively little about them. Recent polls show Canadians as a whole assume that biotechnology is beneficial, and that our governments will regulate it in our best interests.

This paper re-examines some assumptions about biotechnology and the new genetics for Canadians as a whole and for women in particular. Our principal concern is that, within the federal government, the interests of the biotechnology industry may be a greater consideration than the health of Canadians.

This paper is intended as a brief overview of "biotechnology" and the "new genetics," and some of their implications for women's health. It is meant to encourage discussion and critical debate. It examines two main areas of concern — agricultural biotechnology, and biotechnology in health care and medicine. Because of the size of the booklet and the scope of the topic, this cannot be a comprehensive study of all the issues. For example, one important topic not addressed here is reproductive technologies since this issue has received broad coverage in women's health literature.

Definitions: A Matter of Interest

Biotechnology is defined by the Canadian Environmental Protection Act as "The use of living organisms, or their parts, for the production of goods and services." Interpretations of the basic definition, as well as views on the safety of these technologies, are far from consistent and vary according to whose interests are being promoted. Included under the term "biotechnology" are such wide-ranging techniques as altering genes through genetic engineering of species, cloning of plants and animals, and xenotransplantation (growing new organs in one species for transplantation into another).

Those who represent the very profitable biotechnology industry or government departments wishing to promote that industry emphasize the safety and benefits of the technologies to the public and are quick to counter any worries citizens may have. They argue that biotechnology includes such benign and ancient practices as the fermentation of yeast to make bread or beer[1]. However, critics in the environmental and health movements, including both scientists and consumers, argue that it is misleading to put such ancient practices in the same league as these completely new techniques. The potential impact on human health of the more recent technologies, such as xenotransplantation, is of a much greater magnitude, and with far different implications, than these fairly benign older processes.

The term "new genetics" includes specific techniques for intervening in physical and medical processes, but it also reflects a significant world view of human characteristics. Canadian epidemiologist Abby Lippman speaks of the "geneticization" of our bodies and body processes, by which she refers to the gradual and disturbing move towards viewing all aspects of our health primarily in terms of a genetic component, expanding what is called disease and disability and narrowing what is considered normal. She adds that "human biology is incorrectly equated with human genetics".[2]

In this paper, we have included the terms "biotechnology" and "new genetics" together because they raise common concerns. Combined, they represent a disturbing trend towards the medicalization of our health, often at the expense of a more holistic view of the larger, systemic social determinants of health.

The Canadian Biotechnology Strategy: Where are the Women?

In 1998, the Canadian government renewed its commitment to the development of biotechnology in Canada by releasing the policy framework, the Canadian Biotechnology Strategy (CBS)[3]. What was renewed in 1998 was a commitment which had been articulated in policies of the federal government since the early 1980s. The goal of the CBS is "to enhance the quality of life of Canadians in terms of health, safety, the environment, and social and economic development by positioning Canada as a responsible world leader in biotechnology." As such, this framework defines the federal government's role in managing the biotechnology industry, and in managing the development and use of biotechnology in Canada. It also focuses on changing Canada's intellectual property laws in order to facilitate development in biotechnology, and in working to convince the public of its benefits both nationally and internationally.[4]

The Canadian Biotechnology Strategy lacks any attention to the implications of biotechnologies for women. This is despite a commitment by the Canadian government to make all government policies more sensitive to gender by considering the differing implications of policies and programs for women and men (Federal Plan for Gender Equality, 1995). Many women have questions about the genetically modified food we are eating and the genetic testing we are being encouraged to undergo, when proof that these are safe and beneficial has simply not been established.

Why Women's Health?

These new technologies will have a tremendous impact on us all – young and old, men and women, rich and poor, those from developing countries and those from industrialized countries. They have specific implications for women and health[5] for a number of reasons:

1) Women are the primary gatekeepers of health care in the home. Although this role has changed slightly in the past decade, key decisions about health care, food, household products, medical devices, drugs and other pharmaceuticals still remain primarily the domain of women in the home. Therefore, women are a very important group to reach for industries producing new food sources and new health technologies. Women are also an important target group for governments attempting to regulate these products and processes and wishing to reassure citizens of safety and efficacy.

2) Part of women's role as gatekeepers of health in the home involves growing, selecting, purchasing and preparing food. Therefore, genetically engineered foods, their labelling and patenting are issues of particular concern to women, as is the safety of the seeds from which these foods derive.

3) Particularly in the area of reproductive health, women receive a disproportionate percentage of medical tests including genetic tests and treatments. Many treatments and technologies once promoted to women as safe and effective were later found to cause harm: the hormone drug DES, the Dalkon Shield IUD, and Meme breast implants, to name but three. Once again, women are being asked to trust and comply with new technologies such as genetic testing and gene therapies about which relatively little is known. One conference participant referred to this as being asked to "take a leap into the genetic darkness".

4) The health of women in Canada could be improved markedly if we could eliminate or at least diminish the structural causes of ill health such as poverty and violence. Efforts to address these larger problems are undermined when health care funds are instead directed to women's individual biology and genetics.

Why Be Concerned as Canadians?

As the largest producer of genetically modified foods after the United States, Canada is an important player in the promotion of biotechnology and the new genetics. Because the federal government sees these technologies as a boon to the Canadian economy, they have been strongly encouraged and promoted. Commercial promotion of the technology, however, is not the government's only mandate. This same government is also responsible for regulating these technologies as part of its moral and legal obligation to protect the health and well-being of Canadians. Therefore, the government has put itself in the position of having to police the very industry it is trying to promote, clearly a conflict of interest.

As major promoters and manufacturers of genetically modified crops, Canada also contributes to potential problems arising from these technologies in the global South. Rather than creating jobs, the livelihood of farmers in a number of the global South countries are being lost because varieties of seeds that they have planted for centuries have been patented by Western corporations and are no longer affordable to them. Biotechnology is a significant factor in the global move towards the industrialization of agriculture and agribusiness.[6] This trend has serious implications for the sustainability of agriculture in developing countries, and will lead to threats to food security through the loss of the diversity of seeds, negative environmental impacts due to pesticides and other forms of pollution and the loss of small-holder farm ownership and of local employment.

The benefits of biotechnology will only accrue to countries of the global South who can afford to pay for the products developed by the industry.[7] As we have seen with drugs for AIDS, many of the countries most in need cannot meet the prices set by the industry. Commercial interests and profits guide corporate priorities and goals, rather that sustainability and human need.

Patents and Intellectual Property: Putting a Price on Life?

All western industrialized countries have patent laws that enable a maker of a product or invention to have exclusive monopoly control over their product. Patent laws recognize the "intellectual property" that belongs to a person or group of persons. Intellectual property means "the legal rights which result from intellectual activity in the industrial, scientific, literary and artistic fields".[8] Patents are awarded by federal governments, and they give the inventor protection so others cannot profit from their invention for a specific period of time - in most countries, twenty years. Because this protection helps cover some of the costs of developing the invention, it acts as an encouragement to innovation.

To be patentable, a product or invention must meet three criteria:

* it must be novel (i.e. new)
* it must be inventive (i.e. not a discovery)
* it must be capable of industrial application.

Patents made sense in the 19th century when they were applied specifically to mechanical inventions. Although the writers of the laws never intended them to be applicable to living organisms, patent law is exploding in this area today, and it is causing concern. Some feel that many of the biotechnological 'inventions' that are being patented today are not really inventions at all but "expropriations from life", or discoveries.

Patent acts are being seriously challenged by those conducting research in biotechnology in order to extend their applicability to living organisms. In Canada, in the summer of 2000, the Canadian Federal Court of Appeal ruled in favour of granting a patent to Harvard Medical School for the "oncomouse", a mouse genetically-engineered to carry a cancer-causing gene. Because this opens up immense possibilities for patenting any non-human life form, and because some feel this could too easily lead to the patenting of human life forms, the federal government currently has appealed this decision to the Supreme Court of Canada.

To date, a number of patents based on human genetic material (specifically single cell life forms) have been granted in Canada. Pat Mooney, Executive Director of Rural Advancement Foundation International (RAFI)[9] cautions, "Once you accept the patenting of life, there is virtually no way to keep the doors shut on the patenting of organs and any other parts of the human body that have commercial application."[10]

Some governments, with encouragement from industry, are working to alter patent laws through international trade agreements. However, not all countries have patent laws, particularly many in the global South where the concern is often less with innovation than with giving citizens access to goods at prices they can afford. Currently the question of patenting life forms (including microorganisms and plants) is on the discussion table of international trade talks at the World Trade Organization. The United States has been more aggressive than Canada with patenting life forms and there is pressure on our country to do the same. Changes in international trade agreements could give greater control to transnational corporations largely from the global North who could potentially gain patents for products that belong—and are badly needed—in the global South. In practical terms, this means that "harvesters" from global North countries are patenting seeds, plants and microbials pirated from the global South and making enormous profits from them.[11]

Moreover, patent laws do not always necessarily work to the benefit of a nation's health. In Canada, for example, twenty-year patent laws relating to pharmaceuticals favour the large multinational companies. This patent protection also makes it possible for the brand name pharmaceutical companies to charge whatever they feel the market can bear without having to face competition from lower-priced generic products. Patent protection will serve the biotechnology industry in similar ways.

Biotechnology and our Food: Genetically Modified Organisms

Genetically modified organisms (GMOs) is a term generally used to refer to crop plants which have been altered by means of genetic manipulation; that is, the actual genetic material of the cell is changed, sometimes by splicing a gene from any life form—plant, animal, insect, bacteria, or virus—into another plant or animal.

Genetically modified foods are the latest in a series of new products in food manufacturing and agriculture. Some developments in food production and food handling, such as refrigeration, have been a boon to public health; they have undoubtedly saved lives, and improved our quality of life. Others have simply provided us with healthier alternatives, such as the addition of Vitamin D to milk. By contrast, the health benefits of genetically modified foods, such as vegetables with more appealing colour, are dubious at best. It still remains to be seen whether genetically modified foods benefit anyone but the companies that manufacture them.

Genetic engineering in agriculture in Canada and in most of the industrialized world has usually been aimed at making plants more resistant to pests, or more tolerant of large doses of herbicides. Despite these advantages, many questions remain unanswered:

- What are the short and long term health effects on humans of introducing such plants into our food system?
- How will the ecosystems be affected when these new organisms are introduced?
- How will communities be affected when these new organisms are introduced?
- Are there sustainable alternatives that present lower risks?

The transformation of food sources as a result of these biotechnologies has enormous implications for all of us. To take just one example: genetically engineered foods may cause allergic reactions. DNA from an allergen such as peanuts can now be spliced into a food without the consumer knowing – sometimes not until it is too late. This issue requires much more study as it could have vast implications for the scores of Canadians who have fatal food allergies.[12]

While our most immediate concerns in Canada may be whether or not the food we are eating is safe, there are more far-reaching issues for communities world-wide. We have already mentioned how farmers in many developing countries must now pay royalties and a licencing fee for seeds that corporations have been able to patent as a biotechnological invention.[13] Even more alarming are genetically altered seeds that do not produce fertile plants, requiring farmers to buy new seeds every year and/or purchase trademarked chemicals to make them germinate. This practice has been dubbed "Terminator Technology" and the seeds "Suicide Seeds".[14]

Spokespeople for the genetically modified food industry argue that these advances will help to feed the many undernourished people of the world. We would argue that, in fact, the world is quite rich with food. The problem is in the unequal distribution of that food and the poor maintenance of the fertility of the soil. Genetically engineered crops are not the answer to these problems nor the route to sustainable development.

In Canada, sections of two federal departments (Agriculture Canada and Health Canada), one agency (the Canadian Food Inspection Agency), and one piece of legislation (the Canadian Environmental Protection Act) are involved in regulating genetically modified foods. Serious questions have been raised about the impartiality of Canada's Food Inspection Agency since it relies heavily on testing done by the manufacturers of genetically modified foods, and supports its claims that these foods are safe to consume. In 1997, a public citizen's conference in Calgary expressed some of these concerns and recommended that "a Code of Ethics reflecting Canadian values must be developed by the Canadian Biotechnology Strategy Advisory Committee with input from all stakeholders to govern Food Biotechnology."[15]

Women as Targets of Promotion

Women tend to be the purchasers and preparers of family meals. Canadian women need to be aware that they are the primary objects of the publicity about genetically modified foods. Manufacturers and at least some sectors of government have determined that it is they who must be convinced of the safety of this new technology.

For example, early in 2000, a booklet called "Food Safety and You" was circulated to households across Canada, at a cost of hundreds of thousands of taxpayers' dollars. In October 2000, the popular Canadian women's magazine, *Canadian Living*, and its French counterpart, *Coup de pouce*, released a supplement devoted entirely to genetically modified foods. Both the booklet and the supplement are produced by the Canadian Food Inspection Agency, an agency that relies heavily on testing done by the manufacturers of genetically modified foods. Both claim that these foods are safe to consume. Groups who have spoken out against genetically modified foods such as Greenpeace and the Council of Canadians expressed concern that their comments, which were part of the first draft of the supplement, did not appear in the final printed version.

In fact, there have been no long-term health studies on genetically modified foods, so we do **not** know if eating these foods is safe. When testing of new products is done predominantly by the very industry that will profit from their promotion, we need to ask whether the health and safety of Canadians is being given the attention it deserves. We also need to ask why these materials are being produced by CFIA, the agency that is supposed to be responsible for protecting our health. Instead of pat reassurances by *Canadian Living* backed by the CFIA, Canadians need solid research about the health effects of these new products. Equally important, we need food inspection and health protection processes which are completely independent of the biotechnology industry.

These are complex issues with strong feelings all around. The economic interests of farmers who make their livelihood by their crops sometimes dictate that they become pitted against environmentalists arguing against the introduction of GMOs into agriculture. Some people lobby for clear and detailed

Bovine Growth Hormone

Bovine Growth Hormone – BGH - (also known as Bovine Somatotropin – BST) is a hormone that increases milk production in cows. Those who advocate using the hormone claim that cows injected with the engineered version of the natural hormone (called recombinant BGH or rBGH) produce 10 to 25% more milk.

Considerable controversy surrounds the use of this hormone in every country where it is used. Its supporters argue that more milk from fewer cows leads to lower costs to the consumer as farmers will need less animal feed and grazing land. The manufacturers of rBGH, particularly the Monsanto Company, maintain that the milk and the meat from the cows injected with the hormone are both safe for human consumption. Opponents, however, point to a growing body of evidence of ill effects on humans and to certain clearly substantiated ill effects on cows. For example, mastitis (inflammation of the udder) is more common in cows given rBGH. The treatment for mastitis is antibiotics, and the residue of antibiotics may be passed on to those who eat the meat and drink the milk of these cows. (Consider how much milk is consumed by children, and how it is strongly promoted to women of all ages to prevent osteoporosis.) This exposure to antibiotics could lead to antibiotic resistance among those who consume the milk.

Use of rBGH has been approved in the United States; in some states labelling is voluntary and in others it is mandatory. In Canada, rBGH has not been approved for use. The decision to ban it in 1998 followed high-profiled action on the part of six senior scientists at Health Canada. When these scientists realized that the approval process for Monsanto's application for use of rBGH had many irregularities, they blew the whistle, accusing senior bureaucrats at Health Canada of showing "unusual favour" to Monsanto. As a result, the scientists were legally silenced by their superiors. However, after the Canadian Senate Agriculture Commission investigated the issue, Health Canada chose to ban rBGH.

For more information on the government's regulation of rBGH, see http://www.hc-sc.gc.ca/food-aliment/english/veterinary_drugs/bst_in_milk.html.

labelling of all foods so that consumers can choose genetically modified or unmodified foods (currently this is not required in Canada). But labelling does not address the deeper implications of GMOs in foods. Many consumers, producers and scientists want a broader social evaluation of the impacts of genetically modified foods. They want to ensure that scientific research not be influenced by the industries that could profit from the outcomes. Others want 'substantial equivalence' to be the benchmark for the approval of genetically modified foods, that is, a genetically modified crop or other product must be shown to be *just as safe* as its non-genetically-modified equivalent before it is introduced onto the market.

While environmentalists, health activists and a range of other concerned parties attempt to put on the brakes with the proliferation of genetically modified organisms, it is clear that the tide is now moving at a pace which will require greater systemic measures to quell its momentum. To sustain the pressure towards maintaining public health and safety as the highest standard, lobbying efforts must be continuous at all levels of government involved in this issue.

The Human Genome and Genetic Research

The problem with gene research is the same as its beauty. Its intellectual simplicity, its satisfying resolution of baffling medical puzzles with logical molecular explanations, creates the illusion that it will provide us with easy answers to larger human problems.... We are who we are not just because of what our genes contain, but because of what has happened to us since our birth and how we use that unique genetic endowment day after day.[16]

Genes are segments of DNA (deoxyribonucleic acid) that specify one or more functional products, such as proteins. Genes are a major means by which similarities and differences in biological traits are passed on from parents to offspring.

The Human Genome Project, an international scientific project begun in October 1990, has propelled the issues surrounding genetic testing into the common household vocabulary. A key goal of the Project was to map all of the approximately 50,000 to 100,000 human genes, determining where they are located on the chromosomes, and making them accessible for further biological study. In June 2000, the roughly 90% complete sequence of the 3 billion human DNA bases was announced to the world. Although this June 2000 announcement has been heralded as one of the most important scientific discoveries of all time, it is a very early step in understanding the human genome. The next phase of the Human Genome Project will focus on producing a 'functional genetic map' that describes how genes function; this is still decades away.

Canadian philosopher and ethicist Susan Sherwin has raised the need for caution in how we embrace the Human Genome Project.

"The Human Genome Project is anticipated to generate the capacity to engage in a variety of problematic practices that also threaten to have a profound effect on Canadian values. Researchers are…. pursuing the supposed genetic basis of various behaviours such as homosexuality, shyness and criminal tendencies. Before supporting development of further genetic tests we must address a variety of difficult questions: who wants to know this information and what is their interest? What use is to be made of this sort of genetic knowledge? What sorts of conditions should be treated as acceptable grounds for terminating fetal life, for becoming ineligible for certain types of employment, or for denying access to affordable medical or life insurance"[17]

With a growing focus on diagnosing genetic diseases and disorders, it is easy to be lulled into thinking that genetic testing holds great promise for improved health. Indeed for some of those who have access to these tests, it may hold some promise. For example, genetic screening to identify those who carry a single copy of a gene associated with Tay-Sachs disease, an inherited and often fatal condition found predominantly in Ashkenazi Jewish and some French Canadian populations, allows those carrying it to receive genetic counselling about risks to children and, if appropriate (i.e. their partner also carries the gene) and they request it during pregnancy, prenatal diagnosis.

There are, however, some facts to remember when we think about genetic testing, whether it is for pregnant women, for newborns, or for adults. First, to learn that something is associated with a detectable

DNA pattern does not mean that the person carrying the gene will inevitably develop that disease. Nor will this knowledge allow one to predict how complicated or severe the condition will be if it does occur. The genetic nature of a disease is complex: some gene-associated diseases are not inherited but rather result from a mutation in the single egg or sperm cell that results in the development of an individual; some are the result of mutations within specific cells after development is underway. Moreover, even when a DNA pattern associated with increased susceptibility to certain disabling conditions is detected in prenatal life, it may require products from other genes and biological processes for a problem to develop. This is the case for cancer. For many cancers to develop, a cell must undergo several (probably 5 to 10) separate gene mutations. Some of the mutations might be inherited, but some occur from exposure to gene-damaging substances in the environment. We do not fully know how much of each factor is at play and how the two interact.

Currently, genetic testing is being sold as a choice to which women are all entitled. Those doing testing seem to feel that by allowing women to give what they call "informed consent", whether this be in a research study of testing or in a clinical setting, they as "testers" are free of any further responsibility. However, is it possible for a woman to give full and informed consent if she does not have all the information needed to consent? Many of the tests are looking for variations in DNA associated with conditions for which there is no known, or no effective treatment. Others, by identifying a woman who will then be seen as at greater-than-average risk of developing some disorder, may lead to discrimination against her. In these situations, knowing one's status may not be seen as useful or helpful.

The women's movement has argued for years that our options (particularly relating to reproductive issues) have been restricted, therefore we need more choice. This in turn can make it difficult for someone to reject the offer, the "choice" of a test. However, health is not simply a consumer choice, and "choice" is not the basis on which to base these arguments. Informed choice hinges on who is offering the test as well as a full understanding of what the purpose is of the option, and on a woman's ability to act. If the information only comes from those who stand to gain (financial profit, academic success, reduced health care costs, etc.) from the use of the new technologies, then we know all sides are not being represented. Moreover, as Abby Lippman notes:

> ...what seems to be a personal choice (e.g. to have prenatal testing, to take tamoxifen) may really be merely a substitute for societal failures to provide what I truly need (the resources – financial, social, supportive) that would allow me to mother a child with Down Syndrome; the guarantees that the water I drink is not polluted with harmful chemicals.[19]

Genetic Testing and People with Disabilities

Advocates for people with disabilities have argued that genetic testing is a form of discrimination against disabled people. They point out that we are already a long way from collective acceptance of disability as an expression of human variation, and that the emphasis on genetic testing will only set us back further. Catherine Frazee, Canadian disability rights activist and Chief Commissioner of the Ontario Human Rights Commission from 1989 to 1992, made this observation when studying all the documentation related to the Canadian Biotechnology Strategy:

> ...[the word] disability appears nowhere in the documents that highlight the strategy's features, benefits, guiding principles, goals, development and progress.... It is alluded to.... It is implied, surely.... But the shadowy foe never declares itself.[20]

Genetic Testing for Breast Cancer

All women carry some form of the BRCA1 and the BRCA2 gene. When the gene is in its most common form, it is believed to keep cell division in check; when it is in a mutated form, cell growth can turn into cancer. Certain genetic mutations in BRCA1, BRCA2 or other genes, some of which may be inherited from a parent, may increase the potential for an individual to develop breast cancer.

When the first so-called "breast cancer gene" was isolated in 1994, the discovery was seen as a very important advance for women. However, consumer groups and breast cancer organizations have been quick to point out that only 5-10% of women with breast cancer actually carry the mutated BRCA1 or BRCA2 gene, and for those who do, one or more environmental triggers are required for the disease to develop. Similarly, less than 1% of women in the general population carry this mutation, so the actual numbers of women who are good candidates for testing is relatively small. Nevertheless, it is understandable that many women with a strong family history of the disease (e.g. they have two or more first degree relatives — mother, siblings, offspring who are affected) may be eager to have this test.

Organizations that advocate for women with breast cancer (such as the Canadian Breast Cancer Network and Breast Cancer Action Montreal) have been working hard to try to influence policy about this controversial test. They have helped to educate the general public about the limitations of the test, and have pointed out that interventions to predict, detect and treat breast cancer are second best to preventing the disease.

These advocates stress that women who are found by testing to have a mutated gene need to be aware of the following: 1) testing "positive" doesn't necessarily mean that they will develop breast cancer, and testing "negative" doesn't mean they won't; it simply means that they do or do not have one of many possible factors which may increase their likelihood of getting cancer; 2) testing positive leads to limited options – at present these are: a double mastectomy and unproven experimental approaches such as the drugs tamoxifen and raloxifene;[18] 3) testing positive could result in discrimination from potential employers and insurers. Breast cancer advocacy organizations have staged a campaign to help fight that discrimination.

Advocates for the disabled also fear that people who decline to be screened might be discriminated against. Dr. Ruth Hubbard, a scientist at Harvard University, has argued that genetic testing perpetuates the idea that it is more beneficial to society for certain people to have children than others, and for them to have only certain kinds of children. When the Human Genome Project made its announcement in 2000, the Canadian Down Syndrome Society released its official position calling for "regulation and research protocols for genetic testing and gene therapies that will protect the dignity, worth and equal rights of all people, regardless of handicap or disability". As the Human Genome Project generally and genetic testing in particular receive more and more public attention, we can expect advocacy groups for people with disabilities to become even more vocal about what this means for them.

Genetic testing runs the risk of leading us into thinking that a wide range of human problems can be prevented or cured once science learns how to identify and manipulate our genes. Along with many others, Ruth Hubbard has argued that this way of thinking puts far too much emphasis on heredity and keeps us from addressing critical health problems caused by the environment, and by social, political and economic factors.

Genetically Engineered Products and Gene Modifications

Developing ways to produce drugs using genetic technology, and changing the genes of microorganisms, plants, animals and ultimately humans is an important and expanding field for the Canadian biotechnology and pharmaceutical industries. These products and gene engineering technologies are presented as having the possibility of providing therapeutic options for those facing hereditary diseases, as well as for those dealing with diseases where non-inherited genetic processes may be involved (e.g. cancers). The business sections of major newspapers in Canada repeatedly report on "spectacular developments" in this industry as shares "shoot up" for the country's major genomics companies. Is our level of health increasing as rapidly as these stock prices?

Among the gene-based products and proposed "therapeutic" approaches, three warrant particular attention:

"Designer Drugs"

The most rapid growth in the field of genetic therapies is in the area known as "designer drugs". Hormones, drugs, vaccines, and antibodies produced from isolated human genes are the basis of several highly experimental and expensive therapies. The proliferation of these designer drugs raises questions about the allocation of health care dollars in Canada. For example, genetic research has led to the creation and patenting of an antibody-based drug known as Herceptin (generic name, Trastuzumab). It is available in Canada to women with advanced breast cancer who have changes (mutations) in a particular gene known as Her-2. The presence of protein products from this gene are indicative of a very aggressive breast cancer that is likely to recur, since this protein stimulates the growth and division of the cancer cells. Herceptin is a designer drug that has been developed to recognize and then block the activity of this protein. It is a very expensive drug: treatments for an individual woman cost more than $2500 per month. Some provincial health insurance plans already cover these costs even though Herceptin has only been shown to extend survival for some women by about five months. There are also increasing concerns about the toxic effect of this drug on heart tissue. Therefore, while Herceptin has some limited positive effects, one must wonder if its considerable adverse effects – and tremendous cost to the health system - have been discounted at least in part because of the potential for patents and profits to the biotechnology industry.

Gene Transfer.

Although gene transfer has received a lot of media attention, it is still highly experimental. It is, moreover, the field of development which the biotechnology industry is most keen to enhance since its potential for growth is enormous. The basis of gene transfer is recognition that cellular processes can be altered by splicing [adding] genes directly into a diseased or non-functioning organ. Once introduced, these genes can work either to replace something the person lacks, or to alter harmful cellular processes. The aim is to treat or eliminate disease specifically in the person receiving treatment. There is sparse evidence to date of the success of this approach in spite of all the promotion of and attention to it. In fact, some people have been harmed by it; some gene transfer attempts have resulted in the death of the patients. Many questions have been raised about the way informed consent for these experimental procedures has been obtained. Furthermore, the same techniques that might be used to treat disease can also be adapted to "enhance" the functioning of specific biological processes, raising still other problematic issues about this form of intervention.

Germ line Modification/Intervention.

Unlike gene transfer experiments that involve transferring genetic material into mature body cells, germ line interventions involve purposely transferring genetic material into gametes or embryonic tissue. Importantly, this means that these changes can be passed on to future generations, and differs from the interventions noted above which only work at the somatic cell level (i.e. any resulting genetic change would occur only within that individual, not their offspring). When there is germ line intervention, any introduced DNA would then become part of the nuclei of all cells of the developing body—including their reproductive organs and ultimately their gametes. This constitutes a deliberate "engineering" of the human genome and, even more than somatic gene transfer, opens the door to interventions aimed at enhancement (as of height, behaviours), not at the prevention or elimination of disease. There are now many examples of this type of experimentation being conducted on animals. Although germ line gene modification may sound a bit like science fiction, its eventual implementation has been promoted by several high-profile scientists. Many governments around the world have *already* banned it, but its prospects remain viable in the United States where reproductive manipulations in the private sector are completely unregulated. Several U.S. and U.K. organizations have emerged to oppose development of this and related technologies with eugenic goals.[21]

Conclusion

Women and women's organizations have been at the forefront of many campaigns to raise awareness about actual and potential harms to our health, and we must be no less vigilant with the proliferation of biotechnology and the new genetics. In particular, we need to monitor developments proposed in the Canadian Biotechnology Strategy and Canada's commitment to a plan "designed to fit the model of the marketplace, not the demands of healthcare".[22]

A growing number of academics, health care activists and environmental organizations feel that genetics has been elevated to an inappropriate place in our health care system and are dismayed by how genetics and biotechnologies are being sold as a way to improve the health care of Canadians. When we consider the new commitment (financial and other) that Canadian lawmakers and the Canadian biomedical communities have made to genetics, it is also important to ask what is *not* getting done because of this shift. For example, are new technologies such as a testing for certain genetic information being introduced at the expense of cheap and effective programs such as basic public health measures for pregnant women? Are designer drugs being introduced at the expense of environmental clean-up programs?

Over the past 25 years, Health Canada has made a strong commitment to health promotion and disease prevention and has recognized that a multitude of factors—social, economic, environmental, cultural and biological—strongly influence our health. On an international level, Canada in fact has quite a progressive history with respect to understanding and respecting the role of input from its citizens on matters of such critical importance. Focusing so much time, energy and finances on genetics and biotechnology, without more accountability from the populations who will be affected by these changes, runs counter to Canada's broader commitments.

We wish to acknowledge the financial support of the following sponsors: the National Network on Environments and Women's Health (which is financially supported by the Centres of Excellence for Women's Health Program of Health Canada); the Women's Health Bureau of Health Canada; the Medical, Ethical, Legal and Social Implications of Genomics / Genetics Research Program of the Medical Research Council of Canada; the Dean of Arts, the Faculty of Graduate Studies and the Department of Sociology at York University. The views expressed in this document do not represent the official policy of any of these organizations.

Endnotes

[1]"Biotechnology is an umbrella term that covers a broad spectrum of scientific tools and techniques, ranging from traditional uses of living organisms such as yeast in bread or bacteria in yoghurt to more advanced techniques such as genetic engineering. Biotechnology uses living organisms, or parts of living organisms, to make new products or provide new methods of production." Industry Canada (1998) *The 1998 Canadian Biotechnology Strategy: An Ongoing Renewal Process*. Ottawa: Industry Canada, p. 2.

[2]"Prenatal genetic testing and screening: Constructing needs and reinforcing inequities", by Abby Lippman, in *American Journal of Law and Medicine*, Vol. XVII, No 1&2, 1991, pp 15-50.

[3]*The 1998 Canadian Biotechnology Strategy: An Ongoing Renewal Process*. Ottawa: Industry Canada, 1998.

[4]For a critique of the CBS, see "Gender and Genetics: A Feminist Analysis of the Canadian Biotechnology Strategy and Alternative Visions for Community Action" by F. Alice Miller and Marika Morris, 2000, at www.cwhn.ca.

[5]We use the term "women and health" in a very broad sense referring to three concepts: women's particular relationship to health care systems; women's personal and social interests in health, and the impact of policy and technology on women's health.

[6]For an elaboration of this issue, see *From Land to Mouth: Understanding the Food System* by Brewster Kneen (Toronto, NC Press Ltd, 1993), or visit the website of RAFI, www.rafi.org.

[7]Its close sister, the pharmaceutical industry, is far more likely to develop products for those who are moderately healthy in the developed world (top sellers are for hair growth, impotence and cholesterol lowering drugs) than to create drugs for tropical diseases which kill and cripple millions each year in Asia, South America and Africa. ("Drug companies and Third World: A case study in neglect" by Donald G. McNeil Jr., *New York Times*, May 21, 2000, A1).

[8]World Intellectual Property Organization – WIPO Publication No. 476-E, Chapter 1, p. 3 www.wipo.org/

eng/main.htm, accessed September 17/2000. The definition goes on to say "Those rights do not apply to the physical object in which the creation may be embodied but instead to the intellectual creation…."

[9]RAFI is "a non-government organization dedicated to the conservation and sustainable use of biodiversity, and to the socially responsible development of technologies useful to rural societies".

[10]RAFI, "The Mouse that Roared on Animal Pharm: Canadian Courts Rule that Mammals can be a Patented Invention", *Geno-Types*, 10 August 2000.

[11]RAFI estimates that medicinal plants and microbials from the South contribute at least $30 billion a year to the North's pharmaceutical industry. ("Conserving Indigenous Knowledge: Integrating Two Systems of Innovation," UNDP, New York, September, 1994", RAFI).

[12]There are also concerns about the impact on the environment of the introduction of genetically modified organisms. For example, plants that are genetically engineered to be herbicide tolerant can mix with their wild counterparts to become "superweeds", and genes geared to making insecticides may kill beyond their intended targets. Insects (such as monarch butterflies) that thrive on the pollen of certain crops have been shown to die as a result of ingesting the pollen of crops that have been altered genetically. We also know that genetically engineered plants cross-pollinate once out in the field, so eventually it will become more and more difficult to study the environmental impact of the new breeds as they will all be mixed together.

[13]Bringing international agriculture concerns closer to home, the British Columbia-based Basmati Action Group (BAG) is working to raise awareness about a blatant example of "biopiracy" taking place in India and Pakistan. Basmati rice has been grown in parts of India and Pakistan for centuries. In 1997, an American company named Rice Tec managed to secure a patent for certain basmati rice strains in the Western Hemisphere. The Indian and Pakistani farmers now find themselves in a position where they can only continue to grow their rice by buying the seeds from Rice Tec. BAG has launched an international campaign to boycott the purchase of any products of Rice Tec Corporation. Check their website at www.eciad.bc.ca/~lolin/basmati/.

[14]From the RAFI website, www.rafi.org.

[15]For more on this public citizen's conference, see, www.acs.ucalgary/~pubconf/html/ .

[16] Lois Wingerson, *Unnatural Selection: The Promise and the Power of Human Gene Research*, New York: Bantam, 1998.

[17]Presentation by Susan Sherwin, "Biotechnology and Health: The Place of Ethics in a National Strategy", at "New Technologies in Health Care", Congress of Social Sciences and Humanities, May 30, 1998, Ottawa.

[18] For more information on some of the concerns associated with tamoxifen and raloxifene, see "Medical and Non-medical Approaches to Disease Prevention", a background paper prepared by Sharon Batt for the Working Group on Women and Health Protection; to be posted on the Working Group's website in late 2000 (go to www.web.net/~desact, and click on "Health Protection").

[19]Abby Lippman, working notes for workshop, "Canadian Biotechnology Strategy: Assessing its Effects on Women and Health", February 2000, Toronto.

[20]Catherine Frazee, "A Rough Reflective Sketch" for workshop, "Canadian Biotechnology Strategy: Assessing its Effects on Women and Health", February 2000, Toronto.

[21]See, for example, the website of the Council for Responsible Genetics, www.gene-watch.org.

[22]Presentation by Susan Sherwin, "Biotechnology and Health: The Place of Ethics in a National Strategy", at "New Technologies in Health Care", Congress of Social Sciences and Humanities, May 30, 1998, Ottawa.

Glossary of Terms

biodiversity: "The variability among living organisms from all sources including terrestrial, marine and other aquatic ecosystems and the ecological complexes of which they are a part; this includes diversity within species, between species and of ecosystems." (from the U.N. Convention on Biological Diversity).

biopiracy: The theft of biological resources and traditional knowledge from indigenous peoples in developing countries.

biotechnology: "The use of living organisms, or their parts, for the production of goods and services" (Canadian Environmental Protection Act). Biotechnology today is principally about new genetic technologies, and is sometimes called genetic engineering.

cell: The smallest structural unit of a living organism whose nucleus contains genetic material.

cell line: Cells that have been altered to allow them to grow, often indefinitely, outside a living organism under laboratory conditions.

chromosome: Structure in a cell that contains genes.

cloning: The making of one or multiple identical copies, whether of genes, molecules, cells or whole organisms, through use of DNA technology.

DNA: Deoxyribonucleic acid, a double-stranded molecule that specifies the linear sequences of an organism's RNA and protein molecules.

eugenics: The attempt to improve hereditary qualities of a population of organisms by selective breeding or genetic manipulation.

gamete: A reproductive cell, either an egg (from a female) or a sperm (from a male).

gene: A segment of DNA that specifies the linear sequence of a protein. Genes are passed on from each parent to the offspring.

gene transfer (somatic): Genetic interventions used to replace a defective or non-functioning gene or add a new gene to an individual in an effort to prevent or cure a hereditary disease.

genetic modification: A process involving the insertion of a DNA molecule into the cells of other species where it can then replicate itself. Somatic modification affects only the body cells of an individual. Germ line modification also or exclusively affects the reproductive cells, and can therefore be passed on to future generations.

genome: A complete set of genetic material (in the chromosomes and the mitochondria) of an organism.

mitochondria: Special cellular structures that produce energy for cells and which contain DNA inherited only through maternal lines.

mutation: Any change in a DNA sequence that results in a new, often harmful, function.

protein: A molecule composed of one or more chains of amino acids in a specific order, depending on its gene coding. Examples are hormones, enzymes and antibodies.

recombination: The artificial production of new genetic material by joining (splicing) segments of DNA from different chromosomes and/or from different organisms.

"Terminator Technology": "Biotechnology that is used to exert control and ownership rights over biodiversity by producing plants with infertile seeds." (RAFI)

transgenesis: The transfer of genes from one organism to another with which it does not normally breed.

transgenic organism: A new organism produced by inserting genes from one species into another through the use of genetic interventions.

xenotransplantation: Animal-to-human organ, cell, and tissue transplantation, often using genetically modified pigs and non-human primates.

Resources on the Internet

Alliance of Genetic Support Groups
http://www.geneticalliance.org/

Biotechnology Information Centre
(operated by the U.S. Dept. of Agriculture)
http://www.nal.usda.gov/bic

Canadian Alert on Genetic Engineering
http://www.sustainability.com/cage/

Council for Responsible Genetics
http://www.gene-watch.org

Genetics and Ethics
http://www.ethics.ubc.ca/brynw/

Human Genome Project Information
http://www.ornl.gov/hgmis/medicine/medicine.html

International Centre for Technology Assessment
http://www.icta.org/

National Human Genome Research Institute
http://www.nhgri.nih.gov

Office of Biotechnology Activities (in the National Institutes of Health)
http://www4.od.nih.gov/oba

Rural Advancement Foundation International
http://www.rafi.org

The Western Canadian Citizen Conference on Food Biotechnology
http://www.acs.ucalgary.ca/~pubconf/Citizen/citizen.html

Union of Concerned Scientists
http://www.ucsusa.org

Women and Genetics in Contemporary Society
http://www-unix.oit.umass.edu/~fholmes/

NNEWH Publication List

1. Complementary Medicine: A Bibliography. (August 1997) Prepared by Rona Achilles.

2. A Different Prescription: Considerations for Women's Health Groups Contemplating Funding from the Pharmaceutical Industry. (Pamphlet from a Panel Discussion entitled: "Ethical Issues in Women's Health: The Delicate Business of Funding from Drug Companies") Prepared by Anne Rochon Ford. (1997)

3. The Context for Health Reform. (March 1998) Prepared by Pat Armstrong for the Health Reform Reference Group.

4. Strategic Workshops: Planning and Design. (May 1998) A Report Commissioned by the Working Group on Women, Health and the New Genetics and the National Network on Environments and Women's Health (NNEWH). Prepared by Kristine Hirschkorn.

5. The Restructuring of Work and Women's Health: An Annotated Bibliography. (June 1998) Prepared by Joan Eakin, Ann Sylvia Brooker for the Working Group on Women, Work and Health.

6. Estrogen Through the Life Cycle. (Fall 1998) Prepared by Charlene Day and Miriam Hawkins for the Women's Healthy Environments Network.

7. Feminist Research Methodology and Women's Health: A Review of Literature. (October 1998) Prepared by Penelopy Ironstone-Catterall, School of Social and Political Thought, York University with Peggy McDonough, Ann Robertson, Barbara Payne, Barbara Rahder, Frances Shaver and Pam Wakewich.

8. Networking Between Ontario and Quebec Health Research Teams and Francophone Women. (1998) Prepared by La Table Féministe Francophone de Concertation Provinciale de L'Ontario. (Also available in French under the title "Réseautage Entre les Équipes de Recherché en Santé et Femmes Francophone (Ontario-Quebec)").

9. Réseautage Entre les Équipes de Recherches en Santé et Femmes Francophone (Ontario-Quebec). (1998) Prepare par La Table Féministe Francophone de Concertation Provinciale de L'Ontario. (Aussi disponible en Anglais avec le titre "Networking Between Ontario and Quebec Health Research Teams and Francophone Women").

10.   Shifting Connections: A Report on Emerging Federal Policy Relations to Women's Health, the New Genetics and Biotechnology. (January 1999) Prepared by Constance MacIntosh.

11.   Gender, Work and Health: 1994 National Population Health Survey. (May 1999) Prepared by Peggy McDonough, Vivienne Walters, Lisa Strohchein *Note: Only the Executive Summary is available for distribution.

12.   Social Science Perspectives on the Body: A Bibliography. (August 1999) Prepared by Anne Robertson, Pam Awakewich and Lesley Biggs, and the NNEWH Body Project Group.

13.   Women, Privatization and Health Care Reform: The Ontario Case. (December 1999) Prepared by Pat Armstrong and Hugh Armstrong for the Health Reform Reference Group.

14.   Education for a Healthy Future—Training Trainers for Primary Prevention: A Participatory Action Research and Evaluation (PARE) Project. (Spring/Summer 2000) Prepared by Dorothy Goldin Rosenberg for the Women's Healthy Environments Network.

15.   Risks, Rights and Regulation: Communicating about Risks and Breastfeeding. (June 2000) Prepared by Penny Van Esterik for the World Alliance on Breastfeeding Action.

16.   Health Care Restructuring and Privatization from Women's Perspectives in Newfoundland and Labrador. (July 2000) Prepared by Ingrid Botting with support from Barbara Neis, Linda Kealey and Shirley Solberg.

17.   Assessing the Impact of Restructuring and Work Reorganization in Long Term Care. (With Annotated Bibliography). (July 2000) Prepared by Pat Armstrong and Irene Jansen.

18.   Identifying the Gaps in the Immigrant Women's Perspectives in Newfoundland and Labrador. (July 2000) Prepared by the Immigrant Women's Health Centre.

19.   Is there a Method to this Madness? Studying Health Care Reform as if Women Mattered. (August 2000) Prepared by Karen R. Grant for the Working Group on Women and Health Reform.

20.   Trying to Work it Out: Newfoundland Women's Experiences in Small Workplaces. (August 2000) Prepared by Agnieszka Kosny, Women's Health Network, Newfoundland and Labrador.

21.   An Environmental Framework for Women's Health. (September 2000) Prepared by Barbara Rahder, Rebecca Peterson with the assistance of Christy Doyle and Jackie Kennelly.

22.   The Gender of Genetic Futures: The Canadian Biotechnology Strategy, Women and Health Reform. (September 2000) Proceedings of a National Strategic Workshop held at York University, February 11-12, 2000. Prepared by the Working Group on Women, Health and the New Genetics.

23.   Women's Self Care Workshops: A guide. (2000) Produced by the Women's Health Network, Newfoundland and Labrador.

24.   Does Gender Count? Differences in English-Canadian Beliefs, Attitudes and Behaviours towards Breast Cancer and Infertility: Descriptive Summary Report of Findings from the 1999 Winnipeg Area Study and National Focus Groups. (January 2001) Prepared by Gina Feldberg, Lisa Strohschein, Karen R. Grant and Dominka Wranik-Lohrenz.

25.   Biotechnology and the New Genetics. What it means for Women's Health. (February 2001) Anne Rochon Ford. Prepared for the Working Group on Women, Health and the New Genetics (Also available in French under the title "Les Conséquences de la Biotechnologie et du Génie Génétique sur la santé des femmes").

26.   Les Conséquences de la Biotechnologie et du Génie Génétique sur la Santé des Femmes. (February 2001) Anne Rochon Ford. Préparé pour le Groupe de Travail sur les Femmes, la Santé et le Génie Génétique. (Aussi disponible en Anlgais avec le titre "Biotechnology and the New Genetics. What it Means for Women's Health").

27.   Marginalized Voices from the Downtown Eastside; Aboriginal Women Speak About their Health Experiences. (March 2001) Prepared by Cecilia Benoit and Dena Caroll.

28.   Moving in the Right Direction? Regionalizing Maternity Care Services in British Columbia, Canada. (March, 2001) Prepared by Cecilia Benoit, Dena Caroll and Pat Kaufert. With the Assistance of Meredith Bourhis, Beverly MacLean-Alley, Alison Millar.

29.   From Fishplant to Nickel Smelter: Health Determinants and the Health of Newfoundland's Women Fish and Shellfish Processors in an Environment of Restructuring. (April 2001) Prepared by Barbara Neis and Brenda Grzetic, with Katharine King, Jhodi Durdle and Colleen Hickey.

30.   On Veut Savoir et Agir. Guide D'action pour la Santé des Femmes de L'Ontario Francais. (May 2001) Prepare par La Table Féministe Francophone de Concertation Provinciale de L'Ontario.

31.   Portrait de la Santé et de la Qualité de Vie des Francophones en Ontario. (May 2001) Préparé par La Table Féministe Francophone de Concertation Provinciale de L'Ontario.

32.   The Impacts of Policy on the Health and Well-Being of Women Raising Children with Disabilities. (May 2001) Prepared by the Canadian Association for Community Living.

33.   STAR (Sex Trade Advocacy and Research) Training Workbook. (September 2001) Prepared by Frances M Shaver. (Also available in French under the title "STAR (Sex Trade Advocacy Research) Cahier d'Atelier de Défense du Travail du Sexe et Projet de Recherché: Materials pour un Atelier de Deux Jours avec les Partenaires Communautaires").

34.   Women's Caring Work in the Context of the Manitoba Health Reform. (September 2001) Prepared by Barbara J. Payne, Karen R. Grant, and David M. Gregory.

35.   Women's Poverty, Women's Health: The Role of Access to Justice. (September 2001) Prepared by Joan M. Gilmour, Dianne L. Martin, Institute for Feminist Legal Studies, Osgoode Hall Law School, York University.

36. Reflections of Rural Alberta Women: Work, Health and Restructuring. (November 2001) Prepared by Lynn Skillen, Barbara Heather and Jennifer Young.

37. Women's Health Care Work With Children with Cancer. (November 2001) Prepared by Juanne Nancarrow Clarke, Paula C. Fletcher and Margaret Schneider.

38. The Stories that Women Tell About "The Flood of the Century." (November 2001) Prepared by Karen R. Grant and Nancy C. Higgitt.

39. Women's and Men's Experiences of Work and Well-Being Under Municipal Government Restructuring. (November 2001) Prepared by Peggy McDonough and Vivienne Walters. *Note: Only Executive Summary available for distribution.

40. Manitoba Health Care Reform: Perceptions and Experiences among Winnipeggers. (1998 and 2001. (December 2001) Prepared by Karen R. Grant, Barbara J. Payne and David M. Gregory.

41. Voices of Rural Alberta. Funded by NNEWH (2001).

42. The Construction of Disability and Risk in Genetic Counselling Discourse. (January 2002) Prepared by the Roeher Institute.

43. The Immigrant Women's Health Handbook. (April 2002) Prepared by Immigrant Women's Health Centre.

44. Representation of A Women's Health in General Medical Versus Women's Health Specialty Journals: A Content Analysis. (June 2002) Prepared by Jocalyn P. Clark, Georgina D Feldberg and Paula A Rochon.

45. Voices of Women, Poverty and Homelessness in Canada. Prepared by Rusty Neal for the National Anti-Poverty Organization. (Septepmber 2002)

46. Rural and Remote Women's Health in Canada. (October 2002) Prepared by Pamela Wakewich and Barbara Parker.

47. Mapping Research on Women and Health in Northwestern Ontario. (October 2002) Prepared by Pamela Wakewich and Barbara Parker.

48. Health and Safety in the Sex Trade. Researched by Cecilia Benoit, Frances Shaver and Rachel Phillips. (2002)

49. Cahier d'Atelier De Defense Recherché. Prepared by Frances Shaver.

50. Visible Minority Youth Taking Action for a Healthy Future: A guide for Ethno-Racial Training Trainers Workshops. Prepared by the Canadian Centre for Women, Education and Development (CCWED) in collaboration with the Women's Network on Health and the Environment (WNH&E).

51.   Training Trainers Workshops: A Network and the Multi-Racial Network for Environmental Justice. An Ethno-Racial Perspectives Guide. Prepared by: Women's Healthy Environments Network and the Multi-Racial Network for Environmental Justice.

52.   Legal Regulation and Construction of the Gendered Body of Disability In Canadian Health Law and Policy. Prepared by Catherine Frazee, Joan Gilmour and Roxanne Mykitiuk.

October 17, 2003